AIR QUALITY CONTROL

National Issues, Standards and Goals

Prepared by the National Association of Manufacturers
Resources and Technology Department

NATIONAL ASSOCIATION OF MANUFACTURERS
ENVIRONMENTAL QUALITY COMMITTEE
Chairman
Dr. J. William Haun
General Mills, Inc.

STEERING COMMITTEE MEMBERS

John R. Brough
Inland Steel Company

R. E. Chaddock
Hercules Incorporated

John W. Clark
Wheelabrator-Frye, Inc.

Jack J. Combes
W. R. Grace & Company

William J. Coppoc
Texaco, Inc.

W. W. Dodge
Caterpillar Tractor Company

Louis C. Gilde
Campbell Soup Company

Matthew Gould
Georgia-Pacific Corp.

Bernard M. Kostelnik
Anaconda Company

Dr. Joseph T. Ling
3M Company

Earl W. Mallick
United States Steel Corp.

James M. Quigley
Champion International

David Sebree
E. I. Du Pont de Nemours
Company

Dr. E. L. Simons
General Electric Company

J. R. Sweeney
Bethlehem Steel Corp.

Donald R. Talbot
Martin Marietta Corporation

Samuel H. Thomas
Owens-Corning Fiberglas Corporation

Maurice B. Tobin
Potlatch Corp.

H. Neal Troy
Owens-Illinois, Inc.

Roy A. Wells
Consumer Power Company

G. R. D. Williams
CPC International Inc.

ACKNOWLEDGMENTS

NAM gratefully acknowledges the assistance of the individuals who were responsible for the production of this document. For referencing available literature which proved very helpful we express our thanks to Hubert R. Smith, Chief — Air Quality Monitoring Branch, Surveillance and Analysis Division of the Environmental Protection Agency, Region III, Philadelphia, Pennsylvania. We extend our deep thanks to Daniel W. Cannon, NAM Director of Environmental Affairs, who extracted, compiled, and rewrote material from many different sources to create this book. And, we acknowledge our gratitude to Dr. Richard P. Nalesnik, NAM Vice President and Manager of the Resources and Technology Department, who directed this project through fruition.

LETTER FROM THE CHAIRMAN

If industry is to continue to grow and prosper, and simultaneously meet consumer needs, government and industry will have to work together, in a comprehensive manner, for realistic air quality control standards.

Industry consumes 50 percent of the energy used in our country, and, to quote the NAM Energy Policy, "Environmental factors should be taken into consideration in the (government) decision-making process but they should be reasonably balanced with the growing energy needs of the nation."

NAM Members, who employ 75 percent of the total of United States employees engaged in manufacturing and produce about 75 percent of all the goods manufactured in the United States, should be greatly interested in "Air Quality Control."

David B. Meeker
Chairman of the Board

Air and water pollution control facilities cost American industry some $5 billion in 1973 and $6 billion in 1974, according to the McGraw-Hill Company. These expenses don't include the hundreds of millions of dollars spent annually for equipment operation and maintenance.

Further, the Council on Environmental Quality projects that our national commitment to a cleaner environment will be some $275 billion during the next 10 years, about 2.5 percent of our gross national product.

For this reason, "Air Quality Control" is an invaluable source document for the over 13,000 members of the National Association of Manufacturers.

In addition to serving as an introduction to pollution control, "Air Quality Control" discusses the Federal Law and Regulations and industry-control agency relationships.

The topic of air pollution is complex and the problems associated with pollution control are legion; thus, NAM is presenting this publication in an effort to widen knowledge in this field.

E. Douglas Kenna
President

TABLE OF CONTENTS

Chapter One

Variations In
Air Quality

1. VARIATIONS IN AIR QUALITY

Air quality varies throughout the United States. It varies on a geographic basis and it varies on a time basis in any one geographic location. This makes even more complex the complex science or art of air quality management and control.

In fact, air quality is as changeable as the weather, and weather is a major determinant of air quality. This is evidenced most clearly when an inversion occurs. This happens when a layer of thermally stable air traps the air beneath it so that pollutants can not rise through the inversion layer, with the result much as if you put a coffee cup upside down over a burning candle.

A single geographic location in the course of a year may have a substantial number of days of excellent air quality, a few days of poor air quality, and the rest of the days somewhat in between, ranging from good to average. The principal meteorological influences include air flow, topography, vertical mixing, and dispersion.

In considering geographic variations in air quality, it is important to note that an urbanized, industrialized area has certain meteorological characteristics which differentiate it from its surroundings. Generally, the urban area has (1) higher temperatures, (2) lower relative humidities, (3) greater cloudiness, (4) more frequent fogs, (5) less incoming radiation, (6) lower wind speeds, and (7) greater precipitation.

The elimination of, or large reductions in, air pollution can only be accomplished by controlling the sources of emission. The practical problem that must be dealt with, however, is balancing the costs of reducing air pollution emissions against the amount of reduction that is required to achieve acceptable air quality levels. This amount of emission reduction is a function of meteorological conditions and their variations in time and space.

The atmosphere is the medium by which air pollutants are transported away from their sources of emission. For a given source strength, atmospheric movements govern the length of time and the frequency to which receptors (humans, materials, vegetation, etc.) will be exposed at varying distances from a source. Principal meteorological influences include air flow, topography, vertical mixing, dispersion and others described below. While these influences are discussed individually, they generally act in concert. In some situations a combination of influences (for example, limited vertical mixing together with low wind speeds) may set the stage for a serious air pollution episode.

A. Air Flow

The most important parameter in the movement of pollutants by the atmosphere is the wind. The greater the wind speed, the greater the turbulence and the more rapid and complete is the dispersion of pollutants in the atmosphere.

Since *temperature gradients,* both horizontal and vertical, increase during the winter season, the speed of the wind flow is generally increased during this time of year. However, occasions occur in winter when prolonged periods of little or no air motion may occur. A study of the frequency of prolonged periods of light air flow east of the Rocky Mountains in the continental U.S.A. shows that such situations happen most often in late spring and early autumn.

In addition to the seasonal change, diurnal changes in wind flow occur at many locations. Night hours are usually periods of low-level stability at most areas within the continental U.S.A. As a result of the effects of *negative buoyancy* and the increased energy required for vertical motions, pollutants disperse slowly and may be confined in relatively small volumes. The concurrent light, variable wind may even result in a return flow of material across the original source. In contrast, the daytime winds are apt to be more turbulent, of higher speeds, and the vertical movements are enhanced, so that the maximum dilution of material occurs on clear, sunny days.

The local winds may differ markedly from the general air flow that characterizes the region. Along the coasts of continents or of the larger lakes, the temperature differential between the land and water is sufficient to establish local circulations from sea to land during the day and from land towards sea during the night. At most locations, these sea-breeze regimes are well marked only during the summer and are masked by the general wind flow during the other seasons. However, in subtropical areas, such as southern California coastal areas, they may be the dominant weather pattern and occur with almost clock-like regularity from day to day.

B. Topography

In addition to the sea-breeze conditions of coastal areas, the topography of an area may be important. Where the air flow is markedly restricted by terrain, the flow may be persistently and continuously channeled to a single direction or confined in a relatively small area. Within a fairly narrow valley, the characteristic daily wind pattern is a flow up the valley and the slopes in the daytime, due to solar heating, while just before or just after sunset, the wind reverses, flowing down the slopes and into the valley. Contaminants released within the valley may be effectively trapped within a small area for long periods. In addition, the shielding from the effects of general circulation patterns afforded by the valley walls will result in lower wind speeds along the valley floor than would be the case in comparable level terrain.

C. Vertical Mixing

Turbulence, or *eddy motion,* consists essentially of mechanical and thermal turbulence. Mechanical turbulence is induced by the movement of wind over the aerodynamic rough surface of the earth and is proportional to the roughness of the surface and to the wind speed. Thermal turbulence is solar-induced and is a function of latitude, the radiating surface and the stability of the atmosphere. It is at a maximum during the summer on clear days and at a minimum during the long winter nights. When the vertical temperature gradient of the lower atmosphere is greater than the *adiabatic lapse rate,* vertical movements are enhanced, and dispersion, particularly in the vertical, is more marked. On the other hand, in a stable atmosphere, when the temperature gradient is isothermal or positive with altitude, considerable energy must be expanded in achieving vertical movement.

A typical daily cycle of temperature gradient over open country on a cloudless day begins with the build-up of an *unstable lapse rate,* which increases during the daytime owing to strong solar heating and associated well-developed turbulence conditions. Just before or shortly after sunset, the air near the ground cools rapidly and a stable lapse rate or temperature inversion (temperature increasing with altitude) begins to form. The inversion increases with time in intensity and in depth during the night, reaching a maximum between midnight and the time of minimum surface temperature. During this period, contaminants are effectively trapped within or below the inversion layer with little or no vertical dispersion. It should be noted that contaminants released during stable conditions at the surface are not transported aloft; conversly, contaminants released aloft from tall chimneys, etc., are not generally transported to the ground under these conditions.

With the coming of daylight, the ground begins to heat and the inversion is gradually destroyed. This may result in "fumigation," the rapid mixing downwards of contaminants which were released aloft during the night. This condition often leads to high concentrations during the early forenoon, before the vigorous mixing of fully developed turbulence re-establishes itself to complete the daily cycle. This cycle may be broken or modified by the presence of clouds or precipitation, which serves to inhibit the vigorous convection of the daytime, but also may prevent the formation of strong inversions during the night.

In urban areas where pollution is most likely, the typical lapse rate regime of the open countryside is modified, particularly at night. Industrial processes, increased heat capacity of urban areas and roughness of the buildings contribute to thermal and mechanical turbulence, and the enhanced mixing prevents the formation of a surface inversion. This mixed layer, usually 100-500 feet (about 30-150m) thick, is capped by an inversion whose base in open country would have been at ground level. Such a condition may neutralize the advantage of emission from tall stacks, since the pollutants emitted will be confined within this relatively shallow layer.

D. Trajectory Analyses

In most discussions of air flow, it is assumed for convenience that the wind remains steady in direction and velocity over a considerable period of time and an extensive area. Actually, this is not the case and detailed analyses of wind flow must take variations into account. Where the wind flow differs from place to place or with time, owing to pressure gradient differences or topography, meteorological trajectory analyses are extremely useful in air pollution investigations in following the action of contaminants released, or in tracing measured contaminants to their probable source. The computation of exact trajectories requires a large number of accurate wind data, but approximate trajectories can often be evaluated from only a few wind observations and still serve useful purposes.

E. Atmospheric Dispersion

Atmospheric dispersion does not remove air pollution but merely dilutes it through an increasing volume. The processes involved are very complicated and only limited knowledge is available at the present time. Because the use of a formula or technique for quantitatively evaluating atmospheric dispersion requires a detailed knowledge of the meteorological processes involved, it is strongly recommended that all such evaluations be made by a meteorologist.

Pollutants may be effectively removed from the atmosphere by gravitational settling if the particle size is sufficiently large. The smaller particles, which often constitute a large fraction of the material, may be removed by impaction on the surfaces of the earth, on vegetation or on buildings, etc. Perhaps the most efficient cleansing agent of the atmosphere is precipitation. The larger particles are readily scavanged from the atmosphere by the falling raindrops. Smaller particles, too, may be accumulated in raindrops and thus removed from the atmosphere. Some evidence exists that air pollution may itself slow precipitation-forming processes.

The gaseous contaminants released into the atmosphere will primarily be removed by absorption, particularly in the oceans and in precipitation. There may be other means of chemical combinations and subsequent removal, but these are likely to be much less important.

The character of pollutants may be modified by photochemical or chemical reactions or combinations which may accelerate (or retard) the effects of the pollutants on plants, animals or structures.

F. Visibility

Historically, one of the main objections to atmospheric pollution was the reduction of visibility due to the pall that often hung over industrial regions. This reduction of visibility is an important handicap to commercial transportation, particularly aircraft, and occasionally, in extreme conditions, to automobiles. Visibility is not, however, a reliable direct measurement of total air pollution levels, since it is reduced only by the particulate material, such as smoke and fly ash, sufficient to intercept and scatter visible light. Gaseous emissions or radioactive pollutants could conceivably cause more undesirable pollution levels without ever affecting visibility.

Fundamentally, however, the effect of lowered visibility resulting from pollution is important not because of the reduction of seeing distance but because of the reduction in the transmission of solar energy to the ground. During conditions of extreme stagnation, such as the Donora or London smog episodes, the pollution reached such high concentrations that a major decrease in solar radiation occurred. This, in turn, permitted the lower atmosphere to remain stable for longer periods, creating a "feed back" effect.

Chapter Two
Pollutants

II. POLLUTANTS

Although air is generally considered as 20 percent oxygen and 80 percent nitrogen, other substances get into the air, and these are referred to as pollutants.

There are six pollutants most commonly dealt with: Particulate matter, carbon monoxide, hydrocarbons, ozone, oxides of nitrogen, and oxides of sulfur.

Air quality is not a function of source strength alone, but rather of the source strength *and* intervening meteorological and environmental influences.

A. Sources of Air Pollutants

Air pollutants may be classified in two broad categories: natural and man-made.

Natural sources of air pollutants include:

  Wind blown dust
  volcanic ash and gases
  ozone from lightning and the ozone layer
  esters and terpenes from vegetation
  smoke, gases and fly ash from forest fires
  pollens and other aeroallergens
  gases and odors from natural decomposition
  natural radioactivity.

Such sources constitute background pollution and that portion of the pollution problem over which control activities can have little, if any, effect.

Man-made sources cover a wide spectrum of chemical and physical activities, and are the major contributors to urban air pollution. Air pollutants in the U.S. pour out from over 90 million vehicles, from the refuse of over 210 million people, the generation of billions of kilowatts of electricity and the production of innumerable products demanded by every-day living. Almost 300 million tons of air pollutants are generated annually in the United States alone.

B. Classification of Air Pollutants

For convenience, all air contaminants may be classified in two physical states: particulate matter and gaseous substances. The former is often subdivided into solid and liquid particles while the latter is divided into true gases and vapors.

Particulate Matter

Solids:	dust
	fumes
	smoke
	aerosols
Liquids:	droplets
	mists
	fogs
	aerosols

Gases

True Gases:	sulfur dioxide
	nitrogen oxides
	ozone
	carbon monoxide
Vapors:	gasoline
	paint solvents
	dry cleaning agents

Characteristic properties of the various airborne contaminants are important in considering their potential role in air pollution. Among these are:

a. Physical properties such as particle size, shape, surface area, density, electrical charge, radioactivity and vapor pressure.
b. Chemical properties such as acidity, alkalinity, solubility, hygroscopicity, reactivity and corrosiveness.
c. Biological properties such as toxicity, taste and odor.

C. Particulate Matter

A particle is any dispersed matter, solid or liquid, in which the individual aggregates are larger than single molecules, but smaller than about 500 micro-meters in diameter. A continuous spectrum of sizes occurs among the particles in the atmosphere, with corresponding gradations in physical and chemical properties.

Variations in size confer different physical and chemical properties on the particles. It is important, therefore, to be familiar with the scale and size ranges of common particulate substances and corresponding changes in properties. For example:

- A micro-meter is equal to 1/1,000 of a millimeter, or 1/25,000 of an inch. The term micron is also frequently used in the literature.
- Viruses are between 0.01 and 0.1 micro-meter in size.
- Bacteria are between 1 and 25 micro-meters in size.
- Fog droplets are between 5 and 60 micro-meters in size.
- Raindrops are between 400 and 5,000 micro-meters in size.
- Particles approximately 10 micro-meters in diameter are barely visible to the naked eye.

1. Particulate Size Ranges

Coarse dust particles larger than 10 micro-meters in diameter and fly ash, composed of the impurities remaining after coal is burned, settle out of the air quickly. They are, therefore, usually troublesome only near their source. Fume, dust, and smoke particles range in size from under 1 to 10 micro-meters. They tend to travel farther than coarser particulates, depending on their size.

Particles less than 1 micro-meter in diameter (generally referred to as aerosols because they are small enough to remain suspended in the air) move as easily and as far in wind or air currents as gases do.

Polluting particles are composed of a variety of substances originating from the myriad activities conducted by man. Because their size and, to a lesser degree, their physical state influence their behavior so greatly, they are commonly identified by the appearance and behavior of the emissions in which they are contained. For example:

- *Smoke* describes unburned carbonaceous particles mostly 1 micro-meter in diameter produced as a result of combustion.
- *Fume* indicates the solid particles under 1 micro-meter in diameter that are formed as vapors condense or as chemical reactions take place. Fumes are emitted by many industrial processes, including metal smelting and refining, distillation, and removal of solid impurities by boiling liquid materials and condensing the vapors.
- *Dust* is a more general term than fume. When solid particles are more than 1 micro-meter in size they are generally referred to as dust. Dust may be formed by natural processes or in innumerable mechanical operations conducted at industrial and agricultural facilities.
- *Mist* consists of liquid particles up to 100 micro-meters in diameter. They may be released in such industrial operations as spraying and impregnating, or formed by the condensation of

vapor in the atmosphere. As mists evaporate, more concentrated liquid aerosols may be formed.

2. The Properties of Particulates

When a liquid or solid substance is emitted to the air as particulate matter, its properties and its effects may be changed. As a substance is broken up into smaller and smaller particles more of its surface area is exposed to the air. Under these circumstances, the substance—whatever its chemical composition—tends to physically or chemically combine with other particulates or gases in the atmosphere. The resulting combinations are frequently unpredictable. For example:

- Very small aerosols (from 0.001 to 0.1 micro-meter in diameter) can act as nuclei on which vapor condenses. Fogs, ground mists and rain may thus be increased and prolonged.
- Particles less than 2 or 3 micro-meters in size—about half (by weight) of the particles suspended in urban air are estimated to be that small—can penetrate into the part of the lung which is unprotected by mucus, and can attract and carry such harmful chemicals as sulfur dioxide with them. Sulfur dioxide alone would be dissolved on the mucus before it reached that vulnerable tissue.
- Particulates can act as catalysts. (Catalysis is the process in which a chemical reaction is speeded up by a substance that remains unchanged itself. The unchanged substance is known as the catalyst.) An example of this is the change of sulfur dioxide to sulfuric acid, aided by the catalytic action of iron oxides.
- Aerosols can absorb radiant energy and conduct heat quickly to the surrounding gases of the atmosphere. These are gases that are incapable of absorbing radiant energy by themselves. As a result, the air in contact with the aerosols becomes much warmer. Some scientists fear that the increasing aerosol emissions of jet planes high in the troposphere may eventually form a heat-absorbing layer that will diminish the penetration of the sun's rays to the earth.

3. The Prevalence of Particulates

The urban atmosphere is comparatively dense with particulates. Los Angeles estimates its aerosol emissions from gasoline-powered vehicles at 40 tons a day. An average winter day in New York City produces an estimated 335 tons of particulate matter. In Kansas City, dustfall in the winter measures more than 67 tons per square mile each month. In the most heavily polluted parts of major cities, from 50 to more than 100 tons of particulates fall each month per square mile. In general, the concentration of aerosols in the air over a city is related to the size of its population.

Automobile exhaust emits expecially large amounts of very fine aerosols. More than two-thirds of automobile emissions are between 0.02 and 0.06 micro-meters in size. One hundred billion particles per cubic meter of air may be produced from chemical reactors which occur between emissions and other atmospheric contaminants.

D. Gaseous Pollutants

The gases of importance as air pollutants come from a wide range of organic and inorganic compounds. The most common are carbon monoxide, sulfur oxides, nitrogen oxides and hydrocarbons. Gaseous contaminants represent over 88 percent by weight of all pollutant emissions. Carbon monoxide is the most significant, since it amounts to about 55 percent by weight of all pollutant emissions.

1. Sulfur and its Compounds

Sulfur (S), the oxides of which are a major reason for many cities' pollution troubles, is itself a nonmetallic element found in nature either in free form or combined with other elements. It is almost invariably present as an impurity in the coal and fuel oils that are basic to most combustion and power sources.

a. Sulfur Oxides

When fuels containing sulfur are burned, the sulfur joins with the oxygen of the air and gaseous oxides of sulfur are formed. Fuel combustion is the major source of the polluting sulfur oxides, although they are also produced in chemical plants and, to a lesser degree, by processing metals and burning trash. The major oxide of sulfur that is produced in combustion is sulfur dioxide (SO_2), a heavy, pungent, colorless gas that dissolves easily in water vapor to form a solution of sulfurous acid (H_2SO_3). Sulfurous acid, mildly corrosive, is used as a bleaching agent in industry. It joins slowly with the oxygen in the air (or quickly if catalysts are present) to become the even more corrosive, irritating mist, sulfuric acid (H_2SO_4). Sulfur acid can also be formed by a different route. Sulfur dioxide can be oxidized directly (changed chemically by combining with oxygen) to sulfur trioxide (SO_3), which can be either a colorless liquid or a white solid aerosol. Sulfur trioxide is a likely product when combustion takes place with excess oxygen. The change is abetted by the catalytic action of some of the ash residue, especially the iron oxides that form on boiler tubes and walls. As sulfur dioxide leaves the smoke stack it usually diffuses rapidly, so that oxidation to sulfur trioxide takes place rather slowly. But, with time, sulfur trioxide can build up substantially and react very quickly with water vapor to form sulfuric acid.

Sulfur oxides can damage vegetation, fabrics and building materials, limit visibility, cut down the light from the sun, and affect human breathing. At sufficiently high concentrations, sulfur dioxide irritates the upper respiratory tract.

At lower concentrations and when carried on particulates, it appears able to cause still greater harm by injuring lung tissue.

b. Other Sulfur Compounds

Other undesirable sulfur compounds include hydrogen sulfide gas (H_2S), which gives off the foul odor of rotten eggs, and two classes of sulfur compounds called mercaptans and sulfides, which are associated with unpleasant odors such as garlic, onions, skunk or decayed cabbage. These gases are familiar by-products of petroleum refining, kraft pulping for paper production and various chemical processes.

In addition to giving off an annoying smell, hydrogen sulfide can tarnish silverware and copper bowls and, by darkening the lead in paint, it can ruin the exteriors of houses. Fortunately, there is rarely enough hydrogen sulfide in the air to harm either vegetation or man.

2. Carbon and Carbon Oxides

Carbon (C) is a nonmetallic element found either in its pure state or as a constituent of coal, petroleum, limestone and other organic and inorganic compounds. (The term organic is used to describe most carbon-containing compounds.) Carbon compounds are most frequently used as fuels, and the combustion process liberates much of the carbon, either as unburned or partly burned particles or as carbon monoxide or carbon dioxide.

a. Carbon Monoxide

One product of incomplete combustion is carbon monoxide (CO), a colorless, odorless, very toxic gas. No other gaseous air pollutant is found at such relatively high concentrations in the urban atmosphere.

Its effects in the metropolitan air are uncertain. Controlled laboratory experiments show that at exposures of approximately 100ppm (parts per million) most people get dizzy, develop headaches and feel other symptoms of poisoning. A concentration of 100 ppm is not uncommon today in heavy traffic. Some studies have measured 370 ppm inside vehicles in traffic jams. Yet a study of 237 people involved in traffic accidents in Detroit failed to show that their driving ability was impaired by the carbon monoxide in the atmosphere of that city at the time of their accidents.

The fate of carbon monoxide in the atmosphere is unknown. Although more than 300 million tons of carbon monoxide are formed each year throughout the world, enough to double the global concentration in about 5 years, careful measurements have shown that the average concentration has not changed over the last 50 years. What happens to carbon monoxide is a mystery.

b. Carbon Dioxide

Carbon dioxide (CO_2), a heavy, colorless, odorless gas, is formed during combustion; the more complete the combustion, the more CO_2 is formed. It is also formed in nature by the decomposition of organic substances and it is absorbed from the air by plants through the mechanism of photosynthesis.

Carbon dioxide is not normally considered an air pollutant because it performs a necessary function in life processes. Even the increasing amounts produced by man's activities are far from enough to endanger him.

The presence of sufficient quantities of carbon dioxide, however, can have undesirable side effects. In the presence of moisture it converts to carbonic acid and erodes stone. It is partially responsible for the corrosion of magnesium and perhaps of other structural metals as well. And it is believed that the huge amounts of carbon dioxide emitted each day are very slowly heating the earth's atmosphere. In time, some scientists fear, this scarcely perceptible rise in temperature may cause the partial melting of the polar icecaps and extensive flooding throughout the world.

22

3. Hydrocarbons

Hydrocarbons are a class of compounds containing carbon and hydrogen in various combinations. They are found most abundantly in petroleum, natural gas and coal. Some are gaseous, some liquid, some solid, and all in all they make up a vast family of chemicals. There are, in fact, thousands of hydrocarbon compounds. Most of these compounds, fortunately, are harmful only in very high concentrations. A few may be extremely toxic, however, and need to be examined very carefully.

Two groups of hydrocarbon compounds are of great importance in air pollution: (1) the olefin or ethylene series and (2) the aromatic, benzenoid or benzene series.

a. Olefins

The olefins are a group of unsaturated hydrocarbons. (Unsaturated compounds react easily with other chemicals.) Most olefins in small concentrations appear to have no direct effect on animal life, although some cause a general reduction in plant growth. In addition, olefins take part in photochemical reactions with nitrogen oxides and several other classes of compounds. The deleterious effects of these reactions are described later in this chapter.

b. Aromatics

Included in the aromatics are a number of compounds believed or known to be carcinogenic (cancer-producing). The most potent of these is benzpyrene (often written benzo(α)pyrene or 3, 4 benzpyrene). A primary source of these carcinogens is the incomplete combustion of organic materials. In fact, most polluting hydrocarbons are discharged into the air by incomplete combustion. And the major source of this kind of contamination is the burning of gasoline in automobiles.

Hydrocarbons can also be released into the atmosphere by evaporation. The oil industry encompasses many operations that produce hydrocarbon vapors. Among these are cracking (the chemical decomposition of oil under intense heat), gasoline storage and tank truck filling. Some hydrocarbon vapors have objectionable odors; some take part in photochemical reactions; some have toxic properties. Other constant vapor emitters include alcohols, esters and paint and lacquer thinners.

23

4. Nitrogen Oxides

Nitrogen (N) itself is a colorless, tasteless, odorless gas that constitutes 78 percent of the atmosphere. A number of oxides of nitrogen occur, but only nitric oxide and nitrogen dioxide are considered pollutants. These have been called status symbol or jet-age pollutants, because, ironically, only a highly advanced country is likely to suffer seriously from them.

a. Nitric Oxide

The colorless, somewhat toxic gas, nitric oxide (NO) is formed when combustion takes place at temperatures sufficiently high to cause a reaction between the nitrogen and oxygen of the air. Temperatures this high are reached only in efficient combustion processes or when combustion takes place at high pressure. Thus, nitric oxide is formed primarily in automobile cylinders, electric power plants and other very large energy-conversion processes.

In most cities the automobile is the largest single source of this compound. The nitric oxide formed at the high temperatures of the cylinder air moves so rapidly to the cooler exhaust pipe that it is prevented from decomposing back to nitrogen and oxygen, as it would if cooling were slower.

b. Nitrogen Dioxide

Nitric oxide, which is relatively harmless, is the form generally emitted into the atmosphere. But varying amounts of nitric oxide are converted to nitrogen dioxide (NO_2), which causes considerably more trouble.

The oxidation of nitric oxide to nitrogen dioxide is very rapid at high concentrations in air, but is slow at low concentrations except in the presence of hydrocarbons and sunlight. Thus, although more nitric oxide is formed in Chicago than in San Francisco; because of the more abundant sunshine in the latter city, San Francisco has a higher atmospheric concentration of nitrogen dioxide than Chicago.

Since nitrogen dioxide is formed so readily by photochemical action, it is usually thought of as a product of the photochemical process. But actually it may be formed whenever nitric oxide is a by-product of sufficiently high burning temperatures, with or without photochemical action. It is also a product or by-product of a number of industries, including fertilizer and explosives manufacturing.

Nitrogen dioxide is the only important and widespread pollutant gas that is colored (yellow-brown). As a result, it can significantly affect visibility. It has a pungent, sweetish odor detectable at 1 to 3 parts per million, fortunately a level seldom reached in polluted atmospheres.

At sufficiently high concentrations, nitrogen dioxide can be fatal, but such amounts are highly unlikely. Prolonged exposures at ordinary concentrations may also be harmful to the lungs, though little experimental data are available.

Nitrogen dioxide reacts with raindrops or water vapor in the air to produce nitric acid (HNO_3), which, even in small concentrations, can corrode metal surfaces in the immediate vicinity of the source. Vegetation, too, can be injured when it grows close to factories handling large amounts of nitric acid. The nitrogen oxides present in the ordinary community's air, however, are probably always too low to damage plant life.

5. Photochemical Products

The numerous references to photochemical reactions indicate their importance in the air pollution problem. Once they were thought to be of concern only in Los Angeles; now they are observed even in the smaller cities throughout the nation.

Photochemical reactions are a complex series of atmospheric conditions involving hydrocarbons and oxides of nitrogen. The chemical reactions are initiated by the action of sunlight on nitric oxide. Many of the resulting products have been identified, others have not. Two major characteristics of this complex reaction system are the general haziness imparted to the atmosphere and eye irritation. The name "smog" was early given to this condition, since it was thought to be a combination of smoke and fog. Subsequent studies have shown that neither smoke nor fog is involved, but the name has remained.

In general, one or more photochemical smog products, either alone or in combination, can cause eye irritation, breathing difficulty, vegetation damage, deterioration of materials and decreased visibility. Some of the principal features and components of this system are as follows:

a. Oxidant

Oxidant is a term used by many air pollution control experts in two ways: one describes the capacity of certain oxygen-containing substances to react chemically in polluted air to form new products. In this sense, oxidant is a general measure of smog formation activity. The term is also used to describe the chemical substances that make oxygen available for this reaction.

Any oxygen-bearing compound, such as nitrogen dioxide, that takes part in the photochemical reaction can be termed oxidant. But ozone is the substance whose name is used almost interchangeable with oxidant. This is because ozone usually comprises the bulk of the measured oxidant and is an early and continuing product of the photochemical smog reaction.

b. Ozone

Early in the photochemical process ozone (O_3), a colorless, pungent gas, is formed. Ozone is an allotropic form of oxygen; i.e., it is composed of oxygen and will react chemically to form the same compounds, but its composition and properties are different. A molecule of ozone consists of three atoms of oxygen instead of two as in ordinary oxygen. And, quite unlike oxygen, ozone can cause coughing, choking, headache and severe fatigue. It can damage the leaves of plants, crack rubber, deteriorate fabrics and fade colors.

c. PAN and Aldehydes

Another smog product often mentioned is PAN, short for peroxyacyl or peroxyacetyl nitrate. Although it has been studied for only a few years, it is known to make the eyes burn and tear. It has the same irritating effect on the lungs as ozone and other oxidants, and it can damage plants.

Still another group of photochemical products is the aldehydes. These result from the union of certain hydrocarbons with oxygen. They are colorless and, in high concentrations, have a suffocating, pungent, irritating odor. Aldehydes are strong irritants of the eyes, skin and respiratory tract.

Aldehydes are also present in the exhaust emissions of automobiles as products of incomplete combustion of fuel.

26

Chapter Three
Control Equipment

III. Control Equipment

Air pollution control systems include hoods, ductwork, fans, compressors, gas conditioners and other auxiliary equipment needed for effective capture and conveying of the pollutant laden gases to the air pollution control equipment. Examples of specific types of air pollution control equipment applied to control specified pollutant are shown in Table 1.

Equipment used to reduce the emission of air pollutants is selected on the basis of collection efficiency. The factors which affect the design of the equipment are:

- Particle size range.
- Concentration of particles in the gas stream.
- Physical and chemical characteristics of the pollutants.

Table 2 represents an overview of particulate collectors in common use by industry.

TABLE 1. CONTROL TECHNIQUES APPLICABLE TO UNIT PROCESSES AT IMPORTANT EMISSION SOURCES

INDUSTRY: ALUMINUM REDUCTION PLANTS

PROCESS OF OPERATION	AIR CONTAMINANTS EMITTED	CONTROL TECHNIQUES
Materials Handling Buckets & Belt Conveyor or Pneumatic Conveyor	Particulates (dust)	Exhaust Systems & Baghouse
Anode & Cathode Electrode Prep. Cathode Baking Anodes Grinding & Blending	Hydrocarbon Emissions from Binder Particulates (dust)	Exhaust Systems & Mechanical Collectors
Baking	Particulates (dust), CO, SO_2, Hydrocarbons & Fluorides	Hi-eff. Cyclone, Elect. Prec., Scrubbers, Catalytic Combustion or Incinerators, Flares, Baghouse
Pot Charging	Particulates (dust), CO, HF, SO_2, CF_4, & Hydrocarbons	Hi-eff. Cyclone, Baghouse, Spray Towers, Floating Bed Scrubber, Elect. Prec., Chemisorption, Wet Elect. Prec.
Metal Casting	Cl_2, HCl, CO & Particulates (dust)	Exhaust Systems & Scrubbers

TABLE 1. CONTROL TECHNIQUES APPLICABLE TO UNIT PROCESSES AT IMPORTANT EMISSION SOURCES

INDUSTRY: ASPHALT BATCH PLANTS

PROCESS OF OPERATION	AIR CONTAMINANTS EMITTED	CONTROL TECHNIQUES
Materials Handling, Storage & Classifiers Elevators Chutes Vibrating Screens	Particulates (dust)	Local Exhaust Systems with a Cyclone Precleaner & a Scrubber or Baghouse
Drying Rotary Oil or Gas Fired	Particulates & Smoke	Proper Combustion Controls, Fuel Oil Preheating where Required; Local Exhaust System, Cyclone & a Scrubber or Baghouse
Truck Traffic	Dust	Wetting down Truck Routes

INDUSTRY: CEMENT PLANTS

Quarrying Primary Crusher, Secondary Crusher, Conveying, Storage	Particulates (dust)	Wetting, Exhaust Systems with Mechanical Collectors
Dry Processes Materials Handling, Air Separator (Hot Air Furnace)	Particulates (dust) Particulates (dust)	Local Exhaust System & Mechanical Collectors & Baghouse

TABLE 1. CONTROL TECHNIQUES APPLICABLE TO UNIT PROCESSES AT IMPORTANT EMISSION SOURCES

INDUSTRY: CEMENT PLANTS

PROCESS OF OPERATION	AIR CONTAMINANTS EMITTED	CONTROL TECHNIQUES
Grinding	Particulates (dust)	Local Exhaust System with Cyclones & Baghouse
Pneumatic, Conveying & Storage	Particulates (dust)	
Wet Process Materials Handling Grinding Storage	Wet Materials, No Dust	
Kiln Operations Rotary Kiln	Particulates (dust), CO, SO_x, NO_x, Hydrocarbons, Aldehydes, Ketones	Elect. Prec. & Baghouses, Scrubber, Flare
Clinker Cooling Materials Handling	Particulates (dust)	Local Exhaust System & Mechanical Collectors
Grinding & Packaging Air Separator Grinding Pneumatic Conveying Materials Handling Packaging	Particulates (dust)	Local Exhaust Systems & Mechanical Collectors

TABLE 1. CONTROL TECHNIQUES APPLICABLE TO UNIT PROCESSES AT IMPORTANT EMISSION SOURCES

INDUSTRY: COAL PREPARATION PLANTS

PROCESS OF OPERATION	AIR CONTAMINANTS EMITTED	CONTROL TECHNIQUES
Materials Handling Conveyors Elevators Chutes	Particulates (dust)	Local Exhaust Systems & Cyclones
Sizing Crushing Screening Classifying	Particulates (dust)	Local Exhaust Systems & Cyclones
De-Dusting	Particulates (dust)	Local Exhaust System, Cyclone Precleaners & Baghouse
Storing Coal in Piles	Blowing Particulates (dust)	Wetting, Plastic Spray Covering
Refuse Piles	H_2S, Particulates and Smoke from Burning Storage Piles	Digging out Fire, Pumping Water onto Fire Area, Blanket with Incombustible Material
Coal Drying Rotary, Screen, Suspension, Fluid Bed, Cascade	Dust, Smoke, Particulates, Sulfur Oxides, H_2S	Exhaust Systems with Cyclones & Packed Towers on Venturi Scrubbers

TABLE 1. CONTROL TECHNIQUES APPLICABLE TO UNIT PROCESSES AT IMPORTANT EMISSION SOURCES

INDUSTRY: COKE PLANTS

PROCESS OF OPERATION	AIR CONTAMINANTS EMITTED	CONTROL TECHNIQUES
By-Product Ovens Charging	Smoke, Particulates (dust)	Pipeline Charging, Careful Charging Techniques; Portable Hooding & Scrubber or Baghouses
Pushing	Smoke, Particulates (dust) SO_2	Minimize Green Coke Pushing —Need for Collection Techniques
Quenching	Smoke, Particulates (dust & mists), Phenols & Ammonia	Baffles & Spray Tower
By-Product Processing	CO, H_2S, Methane, Ammonia, H_2, Phenols, Hydrogen Cyanide, N_2, Benzene, Xylene, etc.	Elect. Prec., Scrubber, Flaring
Material Storage (coal & coke)	Particulates (dust)	Wetting, Plastic Spray, Fire Prevention Techniques

INDUSTRY: FERTILIZER INDUSTRY (Chemical)

Phosphate Fertilizers Crushing, Grinding & Calcining	Particulates (dust)	Exhaust System, Scrubber, Cyclone Baghouse
Hydrolysis of P_2O_5	PH_3, P_2O_5, H_3PO_4 mist	Scrubbers, flare

TABLE 1. CONTROL TECHNIQUES APPLICABLE TO UNIT PROCESSES AT IMPORTANT EMISSION SOURCES

INDUSTRY: FERTILIZER INDUSTRY (Chemical)

PROCESS OF OPERATION	AIR CONTAMINANTS EMITTED	CONTROL TECHNIQUES
Acidulation & Curing	HF, SiF_4	Scrubbers
Granulation	Particulates (dust) (product recovery)	Exhaust System, Scrubber or Baghouse
Ammoniation	NH_3, NH_4Cl, SiF_4HF	Cyclone, Elect. Prec., Baghouse, High Energy Scrubber
Nitric Acid Acidulation	NO_x, Gaseous Fluoride Compounds	Scrubber, Addition of Urea
Superphosphate Storage & Shipping	Particulates (dust)	Exhaust System, Cyclone or Baghouse
Ammonium Nitrate Reactor	NH_3, NO_x	Scrubber
Prilling Tower	NH_4, NO_3	Proper Operation Control

TABLE 1. CONTROL TECHNIQUES APPLICABLE TO UNIT PROCESSES AT IMPORTANT EMISSION SOURCES

INDUSTRY: FOUNDRIES (Iron)

PROCESS OF OPERATION	AIR CONTAMINANTS EMITTED	CONTROL TECHNIQUES
Melting (cupola) Charging Melting Pouring Bottom Drop	Smoke & Particulates Smoke & Particulates, Fume, Oil, Mist, CO Smoke & Particulates	Closed Top with Exhaust System, CO Afterburner, Gas-cooling Device & Baghouse or Elect. Prec., Wetting to Extinguish Fire

INDUSTRY: FOUNDRIES (Brass Bronze)

Melting Charging Melting Pouring	Smoke, Particulates, Oil Mist Zinc Oxide Fume, Particulates, Smoke, Zinc Oxide Fume, Lead Oxide Fume	Low Zinc Content Red Brass: Use Good Combustion Controls & Slag Cover. High Zinc Content Brass: Use Good Combustion Controls, Local Exhaust System & Baghouse

INDUSTRY: FOUNDRIES (Aluminum)

Melting Charging Melting Pouring	Smoke & Particulates	Charge Clean Material (no paint or grease) Proper Operation should be Required. No Air Pollution Control Equipment if no Fluxes are Used & Degassing is not required. Dirty Charge Requires Exhaust System with Scrubbers & Baghouses

INDUSTRY: FOUNDRIES (Zinc)

Melting Charging Melting Pouring	Smoke & Particulates Zinc Oxide Fume Oil Mist & Hydrocarbons from Die Casting Machines	Exhaust System with Cyclone and Baghouse. Charge Clean Material (no paint or grease) Careful Skimming of Dross Use Low Smoking Die Casting Lubricants

TABLE 1. CONTROL TECHNIQUES APPLICABLE TO UNIT PROCESSES AT IMPORTANT EMISSION SOURCES

INDUSTRIES: FOUNDRIES (Zinc)

PROCESS OF OPERATION	AIR CONTAMINANTS EMITTED	CONTROL TECHNIQUES
Sand Handling Shakeout Magnetic Pully Conveyors & Elevators Rotary Cobler	Particulate (dust), Smoke Organic Vapors Particulates (dust)	 Exhaust System, Cyclone & Baghouse
Core Making Ovens	Organic Acids, Aldehydes, Smoke, Hydrocarbons	Use of Binders that will Allow Ovens to Operate at Less than 400° F or Exhaust Systems & Afterburners

INDUSTRY: GALVANIZING OPERATIONS

Hot Dip Galvanizing Tank Kettle Dipping Material into the Molten Zinc. Dusting Flux onto the Surface of the Molten Zinc.	Fumes, Particulates (liquid), Vapors — NH, CL, ZnO, $ZnCl_2$, Zn, NH_3, Oil, & C	Close Fitting Hoods with High Indraft Velocities (in some cases the hood may not be able to be close to the kettle so that the indraft velocity must be very high) Baghouses, Elect. Prec.

TABLE 1. CONTROL TECHNIQUES APPLICABLE TO UNIT PROCESSES AT IMPORTANT EMISSION SOURCES

INDUSTRY: KRAFT PULP MILLS

PROCESS OF OPERATION	AIR CONTAMINANTS EMITTED	CONTROL TECHNIQUES
Digesters Batch & Continuous	Mercaptans, Methanol (odors)	Condensers & Use of Lime Kiln, Hog Fuel Boiler or Furnaces as Afterburners
Multiple Effect Evaporators	H_2S, Other Odors	Caustic-Scrubbing & ThermalOxidation of Non-Condensibles
Recovery Furnace	H_2S, Mercaptans, Organic Sulfides & Disulfides	Paper Combustion Controls for Fluctuating Load & Unrestricted Primary & Secondary Air Flow to Furnace & Elect. Prec.
Weak & Strong Black Liquor Oxidation	H_2S	Packed Tower & Cyclone
Smelt Tanks	Particulates (mist or dust)	Demisters, Venturi, Packed Tower or Impingement Type Scrubbers
Lime Kiln	Particulates (dust), H_2S	Venturi Scrubbers

INDUSTRY: MUNICIPAL & INDUSTRIAL INCINERATORS

PROCESS OF OPERATION	AIR CONTAMINANTS EMITTED	CONTROL TECHNIQUES
Single Chamber Incinerators	Particulates, Smoke, Volatiles, CO, SO_x, Ammonia, Organic Acids, Aldehydes, NO_x, Hydrocarbons, Odors, HCl	
Flue Fed		Settling Chambers, Scrubbers, Afterburner, By-pass Flue, Ash Cleanout

TABLE 1. CONTROL TECHNIQUES APPLICABLE TO UNIT PROCESSES AT IMPORTANT EMISSION SOURCES

INDUSTRY: MUNICIPAL & INDUSTRIAL INCINERATORS

PROCESS OF OPERATION	AIR CONTAMINANTS EMITTED	CONTROL TECHNIQUES
Multiple Chamber Incinerators Retort, Inline	Particulates, Smoke and Combustion Contaminants	Operating at Rated Capacity, Using Auxiliary Fuel as Specified & Good Maintenance including Timely Cleanout of Ash
Flue Fed	Particulates, Smoke and Combustion Contaminants	Use of Charging Gates & Automatic Controls for Draft
Wood Waste	Particulates, Smoke and Combustion Contaminants	Continuous Feed Systems, Operate at Design Load & Excess Air, Limit Charging of Oily Material
Municipal Incinerators 50-100 tons/day	Particulates, Smoke Volatiles, CO, Ammonia, Organic Acids, Aldehydes, NO_x, Hydrocarbons, SO_x, Hydrogen Chloride, Odors	Preparation of Materials Including Weighing, Grinding, Shredding; Control of Tipping Area, Furnace Design with Proper Automatic Controls; Proper Startup Techniques; Maintenance of Design Operating Temperatures; use of Scrubbers & Baghouses; Proper Ash Cleanout
Pathological Incinerators	Odors, Hydrocarbons	Proper Charging
Wood Waste & Industrial Waste	Particulates, Smoke and Combustion Contaminants	Modified Fuel Feed , Auxiliary Fuel & Dryer Systems
Box Type	Particulates, Smoke and Combustion Contaminants	Allow Proper Startup, Charge Material Slowly, Don't Overload

TABLE 1. CONTROL TECHNIQUES APPLICABLE TO UNIT PROCESSES AT IMPORTANT EMISSION SOURCES

INDUSTRY: NON-FERRUS SMELTERS, PRIMARY COPPER

PROCESS OF OPERATION	AIR CONTAMINANTS EMITTED	CONTROL TECHNIQUES
Roasting	SO_2, Particulates, Fume	Exhaust System, Settling Chambers, Cyclones or Scrubbers & Elect. Prec. for Dust & Fumes & Sulfuric Acid Plant for SO_2.
Reverberatory Furnace	Smoke, Particulate, Fume, SO_2	Exhaust System, Settling Chambers, Cyclines of Scrubbers & Elect. Prec. for Dust & Fumes & Sulfuric Acid Plant for SO_2

INDUSTRY: LEAD

PROCESS OF OPERATION	AIR CONTAMINANTS EMITTED	CONTROL TECHNIQUES
Sintering	SO_2, Particulates, Smoke	Exhaust system, Cyclones, & Baghouse or Precipitators for Dust & Fumes, Sulfuric Acid Plant for SO_2
Blast Furnace	SO_2, CO, Particulates Lead Oxide, Zinc Oxide	Exhaust System, Settling Chambers, Afterburner & Cooling Device, Cyclone & Baghouse

TABLE 1. CONTROL TECHNIQUES APPLICABLE TO UNIT PROCESSES AT IMPORTANT EMISSION SOURCES

INDUSTRY: LEAD

PROCESS OF OPERATION	AIR CONTAMINANTS EMITTED	CONTROL TECHNIQUES
Dross Reverberatory Furnace	SO_2, Particulates, Fume	Exhaust System, Settling Chambers, Cyclone & Cooling Device, Baghouse
Refining Kettles	SO_2, Particulates	Local Exhaust, System, Cooling Device Baghouse or Precipitator

INDUSTRY: CADMIUM

Roasters, Slag, Fuming Furnaces, Deleading Kilns	Particulates	Local Exhaust System, Baghouse or Precipitator

INDUSTRY: ZINC

Roasting	Particulates (dust) & SO_2	Exhaust System, Humidifier, Cyclone Scrubber, Elect. Prec. & Acid Plant
Sintering	Particulates (dust) & SO_2	Exhaust System, Humidifier, Elect. Prec. & Acid Plant
Calcining	Zinc Oxide, Fume, Particulates, SO_2, CO	Exhaust System, Baghouse
Retorts Electric Arc		

INDUSTRY: NON-FERROUS SMELTERS, SECONDARY

Blast Furnaces & Cupolas— Recover Metal from Scrap & Slag	Dust, Fumes, Particulates, Oil Vapor, Smoke, CO	Exhaust Systems, Cooling Devices, CO Burners & Baghouses or Precipitators

TABLE 1. CONTROL TECHNIQUES APPLICABLE TO UNIT PROCESSES AT IMPORTANT EMISSION SOURCES

INDUSTRY: NON-FERROUS SMELTERS, SECONDARY

PROCESS OF OPERATION	AIR CONTAMINANTS EMITTED	CONTROL TECHNIQUES
Reverberatory Furnaces	Dust, Fumes, Particulates, Smoke, Gaseous Fluxing Materials	Exhaust Systems & Baghouses or Precipitators or Venturi Scrubbers
Crucible Furnaces	See Non-Ferrous Foundries	
Sweat Furnaces	Smoke, Particulates Fumes	Precleaning Metal & Exhaust Systems with Afterburner & Baghouse
Wire Reclamation & Autobody Burning	Smoke, Particulates	Scrubbers & Afterburners

INDUSTRY: PAINT & VARNISH MFG.

PROCESS OF OPERATION	AIR CONTAMINANTS EMITTED	CONTROL TECHNIQUES
Resin Mfg. Closed Reaction Vessel	Acrolein, Other Aldehydes & Fatty Acids (odors) Phthalic Anhydride (subl.)	Exhaust System with Scrubbers & Fume Burners
Varnish Cooking— Open or Closed Vessels	Ketones, Fatty Acids, Formic Acid, Acetic Acid, Glycerin, Acrolein, Other Aldehydes, Phenols & Terpenes; From Tall Oils, Hydrogen Sulfide, Alkyl Sulfide, Butyl Mercaptan & Thiofene (odors)	Exhaust system with Scrubbers & Fume Burners—Close Fitting Hoods are Required for Open Kettles
Solvent Thinning	Olefins, Branches Chain Aromatics & Ketones (odors) Solvents	Exhaust System with Fume Burners

TABLE 1. CONTROL TECHNIQUES APPLICABLE TO UNIT PROCESSES AT IMPORTANT EMISSION SOURCES

INDUSTRY: RENDERING PLANTS

PROCESS OF OPERATION	AIR CONTAMINANTS EMITTED	CONTROL TECHNIQUES
Feed Stock Storage & Housekeeping	Odors	Quick Processing, Washdown of All Concrete Surfaces, Pave Dirt Roads, Proper Sewer Maintenance
Cookers & Percolators	SO_2, Mercaptans, Ammonia, Odors	Exhaust System, Condenser, Scrubber or Incinerator
Grinding	Particulates (dust)	Exhaust System & Scrubber

INDUSTRY: ROOFING PLANTS (Asphalt Saturators)

PROCESS OF OPERATION	AIR CONTAMINANTS EMITTED	CONTROL TECHNIQUES
Felt or Paper Saturators Spray Section Asphalt Tank Wet Looper	Asphalt Vapors & Particulates (liquid)	Exhaust System with High Inlet Velocity at Hoods (> 200 ft/min) with Either Spray Scrubbers, Baghouses or Two Stage Low Voltage Elect. Prec.
Crushed Rock or Other Minerals Handling	Particulates (dust)	Local Exhaust System, Cyclone or Multiple Cyclones

INDUSTRY: STEEL MILLS

PROCESS OF OPERATION	AIR CONTAMINANTS EMITTED	CONTROL TECHNIQUES
Blast Furnaces Charging, Pouring	CO, Fumes, Smoke Particulates (dust)	Good Maintenance, Seal Leaks; Use of Higher Ratio of Pelletized or Sintered Ore; CO Burned in Waste Heat Boilers, Stoves or Coke Ovens; Cyclone, Scrubber, Elect. Prec. or Venturi Scrubber

TABLE 1. CONTROL TECHNIQUES APPLICABLE TO UNIT PROCESSES AT IMPORTANT EMISSION SOURCES

INDUSTRY: STEEL MILLS

PROCESS OF OPERATION	AIR CONTAMINANTS EMITTED	CONTROL TECHNIQUES
Electric Steel Furnaces Charging, Pouring Oxygen Blow	Fumes, Smoke, Particulates (dust) CO	Segregate Dirty Scrap, Proper Hooding, Baghouses, Venturi Scrubbers, or Elect. Prec.
Electric Steel Furnaces Charging Pouring, Oxygen Blow	Fumes, Smoke, Particulates (dust), CO	Segregate Dirty Scrap; Proper Hooding, Venturi Scrubbers, or Elect. Prec.
Open Hearth Furnaces Oxygen Blow, Pouring	Fumes, Smoke, SO_x, Particulates, (dust), CO, NO_x	Proper Hooding, Settling Chambers, Waste Heat Boiler, Baghouse, Elect. Prec. or Venturi Scrubber
Basic Oxygen Furnaces Oxygen Blowing	Fumes, Smoke, CO, Particulates (dust)	Proper Hooding (capture emissions & dilute CO) Scrubbers or Elect. Prec.
Raw Material Storage	Particulates (dust)	Wetting or Application of Plastic Spray
Pelletizing	Particulates (dust)	Proper Hooding, Cyclones, Baghouse
Sintering	Smoke, Particulates (dust), SO_2, NO_x	Proper Hooding, Cyclones, Venturi Scrubbers, Baghouse or Precipitator

TABLE 2
USE OF PARTICULATE COLLECTORS BY INDUSTRY

Industrial Classification	Process	EP	MC	FF	WS	Other
Utilities and industrial power plants	Coal	0	0	—	—	—
	Oil	0	0	—	—	—
	Natural gas	—	—	—	—	—
	Lignite	0	0	—	—	—
	Wood and bark	+	0	—	+	—
	Bagasse	—	0	—	—	—
	Fluid coke	0	+	—	—	+
Pulp and paper	Kraft	0	—	—	0	—
	Soda	0	—	—	0	—
	Lime kiln	—	—	—	0	—
	Chemical	—	—	—	0	—
	Dissolver tank vents	—	0	—	—	+
Rock products	Cement	0	0	0	+	—
	Phosphate	0	0	0	0	—
	Gypsum	0	0	0	0	—
	Alumina	0	0	0	+	—
	Lime	0	0	+	—	—
	Bauxite	0	0	—	—	—
	Magnesium oxide	+	+	—	—	—
Steel	Blast furnace	0	—	—	0	+
	Open hearth	0	—	—	+	+
	Basic oxygen furnace	0	—	—	0	—
	Electric furnace	+	—	0	0	—
	Sintering	0	0	—	—	—
	Coke ovens	0	—	—	—	+
	Ore roasters	0	0	—	+	—
	Cupola	+	—	+	0	—
	Pyrites roaster	0	0	—	0	—
	Taconite	+	0	—	—	—
	Hot scarfing	0	—	—	+	—

Key: 0 = Most common   Other = Packed towers
         + = Not normally used   Mist pads
        EP = Electrostatic Precipitator   Slag filter
        MC = Mechanical Collector   Centrifugal exhausters
        FF = Fabric Filter   Flame incineration
        WS = Wet Scrubber   Settling chamber

TABLE 2
USE OF PARTICULATE COLLECTORS BY INDUSTRY

Industrial Classification	Process	EP	MC	FF	WS	Other
Mining and metallurgical. . . .	Zinc roaster	0	0	—	—	—
	Zinc smelter	0	—	—	—	—
	Copper roaster	0	0	—	—	—
	Copper reverb	0	—	—	—	—
	Copper converter . . .	0	—	—	—	—
	Lead furnace	—	—	0	0	—
	Aluminum	0	—	—	0	+
	Elemental phos	0	—	—	—	—
	Ilmenite	0	0	—	—	—
	Titanium dioxide . . .	+	—	0	—	—
	Molybdenum	+	—	—	—	—
	Sulfuric acid.	0	—	—	0	0
	Phosphoric acid	—	—	—	0	0
	Nitric acid	—	—	—	0	0
	Ore benefication . . .	+	+	+	+	+
Miscellaneous	Refinery catalyst . . .	0	0	—	—	—
	Coal drying	—	0	—	—	—
	Coal mill vents	—	+	0	—	—
	Municipal incinerators	+	0	—	0	+
	Carbon black	+	+	+	—	—
	Apartment incinerators	—	—	—	0	—
	Spray drying	—	0	0	+	—
	Machining operation.	—	0	0	+	+
	Hot coating	—	—	—	0	0
	Precious metal	0	—	0	—	—
	Feed and flour milling	—	0	0	—	—
	Lumber mills	—	0	—	—	—
	Wood working	—	0	0	—	—

Key: 0 = Most common   Other = Packed towers
       + = Not normally used   Mist pads
      EP = Electrostatic Precipitator   Slag filter
      MC = Mechanical Collector   Centrifugal exhausters
      FF = Fabric Filter   Flame incineration
      WS = Wet Scrubber   Settling chamber

Chapter Four

Measurement
of Pollutants

IV. MEASUREMENT OF POLLUTANTS

American industry has developed a wide variety of instruments to sample, measure and monitor pollutants both in stack gases and in the ambient air.

One company lists among its air and gas samplers the following:

AISI Smoke Samplers, AISI H_2S Samplers, AISI Automatic Stack Monitor, Sequential Dust and Gas Samplers, Portable Samplers, Portable Pressure/Vacuum Pumps, SO_2 (lead candle) Stations, Dust Fall Jars, Spot Evaluators, Stack Samplers, Samplers with Alert and Telemetering, Mobile & Stationary Sampling Units, SO_2 Analyzer Recorders, Gas Bubbler Samplers, Radioactive Dust Samplers, Flow Meters and Accessories, Filter Holders, High Volume Samplers, Alarm Samplers, Meteorological Systems.

Measurements of air pollutants may be in terms of concentrations or weights or rates. Concentrations may be expressed in terms of parts per million (ppm) or parts per billion (ppb). Weights may be expressed in micrograms per cubic meter (ug/m^3) for airborne pollutants or tons per square mile (dustfall). Rates may be expressed in pounds per hour (emission rate) or pounds per unit of product (process rate) or tons per square mile per month or per year (monthly or yearly rate of dustfall). The following are some common metric conversions for a number of air pollutants:

AIR QUALITY DATA (25° C; 760 mm Hg)
ppm SO_2 x 2620 = ug/m^3 SO_2 (Sulfur Dioxide)
ppm CO x 1150 = ug/m^3 CO (Carbon monoxide)
ppm CO_x x 1.15= mg/m^3 CO (Carbon monoxide)
ppm CO_2 x 1800 = ug/m^3 CO_2 (Carbon dioxide)
ppm CO_2 x 1.8 = mg/m^3 CO_2 (Carbon dioxide)
ppm NO x 1230 = ug/m^3 NO (Nitrogen Oxide)
ppm NO_2 x 1880 = ug/m^3 NO_2 (Nitrogen Dioxide)
ppm O_3 x 1960 = ug/m^3 O_3 (Ozone)
ppm CH_4 x 655 = ug/m^3 CH_4 (Methane)
ppm CH_4 x 655 = mg/m^3 CH_4 (Methane)
ppm CH_3SH x 2000 = ug/m^3 CH_3SH (Methyl mercaptan)
ppm C_3H_8 x 1800 = ug/m^3 C_3H_8 (Propane)
ppm C_3H_8 x 1.8 = mg/m^3 C_3H_8 (Propane)
ppm F-x 790 = ug/m^3 F- (Fluoride)
ppm H_2S x 1400 = ug/m^3 H_2S (Hydrogen Sulfide)
ppm NH_3 x 696 = ug/m^3 NH_3 (Ammonia)
ppm HCHO x 1230 = ug/m^3 HCHO (Formaldehyde)

The following are some conversion factors for common air pollution measurements.

To convert from	To	Multiply by
	DUSTFALL	
Tons/sq mile	Pounds/acre	3.125
	Pounds/1000 sq ft	0.07174
	Grams/sq m	0.3503
	Kilograms/sq km	350.3
	Milligrams/sq m	350.3
	Milligrams/sq m	0.03503
	Grams/sq ft	0.03254
Pounds/acre	Tons/sq mile	0.32
	Pounds/1000 sq ft	0.023
	Grams/sq m	0.1121
	Kilograms/sq km	112.1
	Milligrams/sq m	112.1
	Milligrams/sq cm	0.01121
	Grams/sq ft	0.0104
Pounds/1000 sq ft	Tons/sq mile	13.94
	Pounds/acre	43.56
	Grams/sq m	4.882
	Kilograms/sq km	4882.4
	Milligrams/sq m	4882.4
	Milligrams/sq cm	0.4882
	Grams/sq ft	0.4536
Grams/sq m	Tons/sq mile	2.855
	Pounds/acre	8.921
	Pounds/1000 sq ft	0.2048
	Kilograms/sq km	1000.
	Milligrams/sq m	1000.
	Milligrams/sq cm	0.1
	Grams/sq ft	0.0929
Kilograms/sq km	Tons/sq mile	2.855×10^{-3}
	Pounds/acre	8.921×10^{-3}
	Pounds/1000 sq ft	204.8×10^{-6}
	Grams/sq m	0.001
	Kilograms/sq km	1.0
	Milligrams/sq cm	0.0001
	Grams/sq ft	92.9×10^{-6}

To Convert from	To	Multiply by
	DUSTFALL	
Milligrams/sq cm	Tons/sq mile	2.855×10^{-3}
	Pounds/acre	8.921×10^{-3}
	Pounds/1000 sq ft	204.8×10^{-6}
	Grams/sq m	0.001
	Kilograms/sq km	1.0
	Milligrams/sq m	0.0001
	Grams/sq ft	92.9×10^{-6}
Grams/sq ft	Tons/sq mile	30.73
	Pounds/acre	96.154
	Pounds/1000 sq ft	2.204
	Grams/sq m	10.764
	Kilograms/sq km	10.764×10^{3}
	Milligrams/sq m	10.764×10^{3}
	Milligrams/sq cm	1.764

AIRBORNE PARTICULATE MATTER

To convert from	To	Multiply by
Milligrams/cu m	Grams/cu ft	283.2×10^{-6}
	Grams/cu m	0.001
	Micrograms/cu m	1000.0
	Micrograms/cu ft	28.32
	Pounds/1000 cu ft	62.43×10^{-6}
Grams/cu ft	Milligrams/cu m	35.3145×10^{3}
	Grams/cu m	35.314
	Micrograms/cu m	35.314×10^{6}
	Micrograms/cu ft	1.0×10^{6}
	Pounds/1000 cu ft	2.2046

American industry is continuing to work on research and development to achieve improvements in measuring and monitoring instruments, especially in precision of measurement and sensitivity of detection at extremely low levels. An atomic age technique is use of nuclear activation analysis to establish the fingerprints of particular mixtures of pollutants. Accuracy of monitoring is essential not only to detect trends toward periods of poor air quality, but also to make sound studies of regional air quality patterns on which air diffusion models may be established to make possible truly scientific air quality management within a particular region.

The most comprehensive regional air monitoring system is being established in the St. Louis area under a program known as the Regional Air Pollution Study (RAPS). This will consist of 24 monitoring stations located at carefully chosen radii from the central station. These ground stations will be supplemented by measurements taken by helicopters and airplanes. Sixteen parameters will be measured, some at one-minute intervals. All data will be transmitted to a central computer for quick, accurate analysis.

The RAPS project is being supported by a $22 million grant by the United States Environmental Protection Agency.

Chapter Five
Federal Legislation

V. FEDERAL LEGISLATION

A sweeping Federal-State air pollution control program is being carried out under legislation known as the Clean Air Amendments of 1970.

This legislation was a drastic overhaul of the pre-existing Clean Air Act of 1963 and Air Quality Act of 1967. Perhaps the greatest change was the provision for national primary and secondary ambient air quality standards to be set by the EPA Administrator rather than having the ambient air quality standards set by each State for each air quality control region within its boundaries. The national primary standards shall be those requisite to protect public health, allowing an adequate margin of safety. The secondary standards shall be those requisite to protect the public welfare from any known or anticipated adverse effects associated with the presence of such air pollutant in the ambient air.

The Clean Air Amendments of 1970 carries over all air quality control regions designated under the Air Quality Act of 1967; provides that the portion of any State which is not part of a designated region shall be an air quality control region; and gives the EPA Administrator supplementary authority to designate as regions any interstate area or major intrastate area which he deems necessary or appropriate for the attainment or maintenance of ambient air quality standards.

Within nine months after the EPA Administrator promulgates a national ambient air quality standard, it is incumbent on each State to submit to the Administrator a plan for the implementation, maintenance and enforcement of the standard in each air quality control region within the State.

Within four months after the submission of a plan, the Administrator must approve or disapprove such plan or each portion thereof if he determines it was adopted after reasonable notice and hearing and that:

A. It provides for the attainment of a primary standard as expeditiously as possible but not later than three years after approval, and provides for the attainment of a secondary standard within a reasonable time.

B. It includes emission limitations, schedules, and timetables for compliance with such limitations, and such other measures as may be necessary to insure attainment and maintenance of such primary or secondary standard, including, but not limited to, land-use and transportation controls.

C. In includes provision for establishment and operation of appropriate devices, methods, systems, and procedures necessary to (i) monitor, compile, and analyze data on ambient air quality and, (ii) upon request, make such data available to the Administrator.

D. It includes a procedure for review (prior to construction or modification of the location of new sources. Such procedure shall provide for adequate authority to prevent the construction or modification of any new source at any location which the State determines will prevent the attainment or maintenance within any air quality control region within such State of a national ambient air quality primary or secondary standard, and require that prior to commencing construction or modification of the source, the owner or operator shall submit to the State such information as may be necessary to permit the State to make such a determination.

E. It contains adequate provisions for intergovernmental cooperation, including measures necessary to insure that emissions from any air quality control region will not interfere with the attainment or maintenance of a primary or secondary standard in any portion of the region located in another State or in any other air quality control region.

F. It provides (i) necessary assurances that the State will have adequate personnel, funding, and authority to carry out such implementation plan; (ii) requirements for installation of equipment by owners or operators of stationary sources to monitor emissions from such sources; (iii) for periodic reports on the nature and amounts of such emissions; (iv) that such reports shall be correlated by the State agency with any emission limitations or standards established pursuant to the Act, which reports shall be available at reasonable times for public inspection; and (v) for authority, in the case of imminent and substantial endangerment to the health of persons, to bring suit to immediately restrain any person causing or contributing to the alleged pollution to stop the emission of air pollutants or to take such other action as may be necessary, and for adequate contingency plans to implement such authority.

G. It provides to the extent necessary and practicable, for periodic inspection and testing of motor vehicles to enforce compliance with applicable emission standards.

H. It provides for revisions, after public hearings, when necessary to take account of revisions of primary or secondary standards or more expeditious methods of achieving them; or whenever the Administrator finds that the plan is inadequate to achieve them.

If a State defaults in regard to an implementation plan, or portion thereof, the Administrator may propose a plan or a part of a plan.

Upon application of a Governor of a State, the Administrator, under certain circumstances, may extend the three-year period for attainment of a primary standard for not more than two years.

Other important features of the 1970 law are authority for the Administrator to establish standards of performance for new stationary sources and national emission standards for hazardous air pollutants.

A standard of performance is a standard for emissions of air pollutants which reflects the degree of emission limitations achievable through the application of the best system of emission reduction which (taking into account the cost of achieving such reduction) the Administrator determines has been adequately demonstrated.

Standards of performance also apply to modifications of old sources. A modification is a physical change or a change in method of operation which increases the amount of an air pollutant emitted or which results in the emission of an air pollutant not previously emitted.

A hazardous air pollutant means an air pollutant to which no ambient air quality standard is applicable and which in the judgement of the Administrator may cause, or contribute to, an increase in mortality or an increase in serious irreversible, or incapacitating reversible, illness. The Administrator is required to set emission standards for such pollutants at levels which in his judgement provide an ample margin of safety to protect the public health from such hazardous air pollutants.

The 1970 law also contains provisions for Federal enforcement; inspections, monitoring and entry; citizen suits; control of pollution from Federal facilities; and numerous other provisions. The authorization provision of the law was scheduled to expire on June 30, 1974, but the Congress extended it for one year.

Chapter Six

Federal Regulations

VI. FEDERAL REGULATIONS

Since enactment of the Clean Air Amendments of 1970, the Environmental Protection Agency has proposed and promulgated a veritable flood of regulations called for by that law.

Perhaps the most significant were those establishing national primary and secondary ambient air quality standards for six major pollutants.

The national primary ambient air quality standards for sulfur oxides, measured as sulfur dioxide by the reference method described in the regulations, or by an equivalent method, are:

(a) 80 micrograms per cubic meter (0.03 p.p.m.) — annual arithmetic mean.

(b) 365 micrograms per cubic meter (0.14 p.p.m.) — maximum 24-hour concentration not to be exceeded more than once per year.

The national secondary ambient air quality standard for sulfur oxides, measured as sulfur dioxide by the reference method described in the regulations, or by an equivalent method, is 1,300 micrograms per cubic meter (0.5 p.p.m.) maximum 3-hour concentration not to be exceeded more than once per year.

The national primary ambient air quality standards for particulate matter, measured by the reference method described in the regulations, or by an equivalent method, are:

(a) 75 micrograms per cubic meter — annual geometric mean.

(b) 260 micrograms per cubic meter — maximum 24-hour concentration not to be exceeded more than once per year.

The national secondary ambient air quality standards for particulate matter are:

(a) 60 micrograms per cubic meter annual geometric mean, as a guide to be used in assessing implementation plans to achieve the 24-hour standard.

(b) 150 micrograms per cubic meter — maximum 24-hour concentration not to be exceeded more than once per year.

The national primary and secondary ambient air quality standards for carbon monoxide, measured by the reference method described in the regulations, or by an equivalent method, are:

(a) 10 milligrams per cubic meter (9 p.p.m.) — maximum 8-hour concentration not to be exceeded more than once per year.

(b) 40 milligrams per cubic meter (35 p.p.m.) — maximum 1-hour concentration not to be exceeded more than once per year.

The national primary and secondary ambient air quality standard for photochemical oxidants, measured and corrected for interferences due to nitrogen oxides and sulfur dioxide by the reference method described in the regulations, or by an equivalent method, is: 160 micrograms per cubic meter (0.08 p.p.m.) — maximum 1-hour concentration not to be exceeded more than once per year.

The hydrocarbons standard is for use as a guide in devising implementation plans to acheive oxidant standards. The national primary and secondary ambient air quality standard for hydrocarbons, measured and corrected for methane by the reference method described in the regulations, or by an equivalent method, is: 160 micrograms per cubic meter (0.24 p.p.m.) — maximum 3-hour concentration (6 to 9 a.m.) not to be exceeded more than once per year.

The national primary and secondary ambient air quality standard for nitrogen oxide, measured by the reference method described in the regulations, or by an equivalent method, is: 100 micrograms per cubic meter (0.05 p.p.m.) — annual arithmetic mean.

Thus, the national air quality goals or objectives for the United States have been established. The means of achieving the objectives vary among the 247 Air Quality Control Regions presently established. In some of these air quality control regions, the objectives will be achieved through considerable industry-government cooperation and considerable expenditure of money, mostly by industry and its customers.

In some other regions, the air quality is already better than that called for by national standards. A controversy has arisen out of court decisions that these regions must maintain air quality at these better levels and not permit "significant deterioration" even though national standards are not violated. Defenders of this "nondegrada-tion" principle say that it is necessary to preserve air quality in recreational areas such as national parks. Those opposed say it will prevent needed economic development in rural and depressed areas. EPA has proposed reguulations to implement the "nondegradation" decision, but they seem destined for further litigation. In the original litigation, the Supreme Court split 4-4, and so did not write any opinion which would shed any light on just what is "significant deterioration." The other puzzling aspect of the decision is that it seems so clear that one of the Congress' big objectives in going to the 1970 law was to establish uniform national air quality standards rather than air quality standards on a region-by-region basis. Although EPA appealed the "nondegradation" case all the way to the Supreme Court it did not support corrective legislation recom-mended by the White House.

In still other regions, it appears that some air quality standards will not be achieved within the three year deadline period or even within the possible two-year extension period. EPA has recognized this "collision course" and has supported legislation to authorize setting of compliance dates for individual sources beyond the dates set for achievement of ambient air quality objectives, on the grounds of shortages of "clean" fuels and shortages of air pollution control equipment.

However, EPA is claiming that a solution to the lack of "clean" fuels is the use of flue gas desulfurization technology which it says will permit the burning of huge amounts of Eastern United States high-sulfur bituminous coal and alleviate the "energy crisis." This viewpoint has been strongly opposed by viewpoints that such technology is astronomically costly, operationally unreliable, exces-sively consumptive of energy, and excessively polluting in terms of the massive amounts of sludge and slurry solid wastes. This issue likewise appears destined for final resolution only through litigation.

EPA has also promulgated regulations for standards of performance for some new sources as follows:

(1) Fossil-Fuel Fired Steam Generators of more than 250 million B.T.U. per hour heat input-emission standards for particulate matter, sulfur dioxide, and nitrogen oxides, generally in terms of pounds per million B. t. u. heat input. There are also provisions for emission and fuel monitoring and test methods and procedures.

(2) Incinerators of more than 50 tons per day charging rate-emission standard for particulate matter which is expressed as 0.08 grain per standard cubic foot (0.18 gram per normal cubic meter) corrected to 12 percent CO, maximum 2-hour average.

(3) Portland Cement Plants — emission standard for particulate matter expressed in terms of pounds per ton of feed to the kiln, maximum 2-hour average, and in terms of percent opacity. Also contains provisions for monitoring of operations and for test methods and procedures.

(4) Nitric Acid Plants — emission standard for nitrogen oxides in terms of pounds per ton of acid produced, maximum 2-hour average, expressed as NO_2, and in terms of percent opacity. Also contains provisions for emission monitoring and for test methods and procedures.

(5) Sulfuric Acid Plants — emission standard for sulfur dioxide in terms of pounds per ton of acid produced, maximum 2-hour average, and for acid mist in terms of pounds per ton of acid produced, maximum 2-hour average, expressed as H_2SO_4, and in terms of percent opacity. Also contains provisions for emission monitoring and test methods and procedures.

Standards of performance for New Stationary Sources have also been promulgated for Asphalt Concrete Plants, Petroleum Refineries, Storage Vessels for Petroleum Liquids, Secondary Lead Smelters, Secondary Brass and Bronze Ingot Production Plants, Iron and Steel Plants, and Sewage Treatment Plants.

In regard to hazardous air pollutants, EPA has established emission standards in regard to the following:

(1) Asbestos — emission standard for asbestos, generally in terms of no visible emissions or use of air-cleaning methods. Also contains provisions for reporting.

(2) Beryllium — an emission standard for beryllium in terms of grams per 24-hour period. Also contains provisions for stack sampling. There are separate provisions applying to Beryllium Rocket Motor Firing.

(3) Mercury — emission standard for mercury expressed in terms of grams per 24-hour period. Also contains provisions for stack sampling.

EPA has also established "Air Pollution Stationary Source Test Methods," published as an Appendix to its New Stationary Source Standards, and regulations governing "Air Pollution from Federal Government Agencies."

EPA's regulations approving or disapproving State Air Implementation Plans are so voluminous that it is impracticable to summarize them.

The following are emission limits attainable by available technology according to EPA's regulations for preparation, adoption, and submittal of the implementation plans:

Type of Emissions	Source	Limits Attainable
Visible emissions	Industrial stacks	Less than No. 1 Ringelmann or 20 percent opacity except for periods up to 3 minutes in any 60 minute period.
	Gasoline powered motor vehicles	No visible emissions except for periods up to 5 seconds.
	Diesel powered motor vehicles	No. 1 Ringelmann or 20 percent opacity except for periods up to 5 seconds.
Particulate matter	Incinerators	0.1 pounds per 100 pounds of refuse charged.
	Fuel burning equipment (solid fuel)	0.1 pounds per million Btu.
	Process industries	Emission rate, E, in pounds per hour, given in terms of process. Weight rate P, in pounds per hour, is $E = 3.59\ P^{0.62}$ if P is 60,000 or less. $E = 17.31\ P^{0.16}$ if P is more than 60,000.
Sulfur oxides	Fuel combustion (Solid fuel)	1.2 pounds SO_2 per million Btu.

Type of Emissions	Source	Limits Attainable
Sulfur Oxides	(Liquid fuel)	0.8 pounds SO_2 per million Btu.
	Sulfuric acid plants	6.5 pounds per ton of 100 percent acid produced.
	Sulfur recovery plants	0.01 pound SO_2 per pound of sulfur processed.
	Non-ferrous smelters	
	Copper	$Y = 0.2 X$
	Zinc	$Y = 0.564 X^{0.85}$
	Lead	$Y = 0.98 X^{0.77}$
		Where X is total sulfur fed to the smelter and Y is sulfur dioxide emissions, both in pounds per hour.
	Sulfite pulp mills (certain sources)	9 pounds per air-dried ton of pulp produced (with new recovery systems) 20 pounds per air-dried ton (with existing recovery systems).
	Refinery process gas streams	Equivalent to 10 grains of hydrogen sulfide per 100 standard cubic feet of gas.
Total reduced sulfur	Kraft pulp mills (recovery furnace)	0.1 pounds TRS per air-dried ton of unbleached pulp (existing recovery furnace).
		0.5 pounds TRS per air-dried ton of unbleached pulp (new recovery furnace).
Oxides of nitrogen	Fuel-burning equipment (gas-fired)	0.2 pounds (calculated as NO_2) per million Btu.
	Fuel-burning equipment (oil-fired)	0.3 pounds (calculated as NO_2) per million Btu.
	Nitric acid manufacture	5.5 pounds (calculated as NO_2) per ton of 100 percent acid produced.

Chapter Seven

Federal and State
Agency Organization

VII. FEDERAL AND STATE AGENCY ORGANIZATION

The following material is intended to convey some idea of the organization of EPA and of State and local air pollution control agencies.

The organization of air pollution control agencies varies considerably depending on the hierarchy of the state or local government. Agencies located within health departments are generally organized as sub-unit functions served by laboratory and administrative services provided by other sub-units. Separate agencies such as Departments of Air and Water Programs are generally organized as self-supporting entities with functional responsibilities aligned within the program. See Figure 1.

In theory, the organizational configuration of the agency has minimal influence on the effectiveness of the operation. In practice, however, a significant number of functional weaknesses can be traced to poor organizational structure and are frequently compounded by poorly defined responsibilities. An effective control agency *needs:* (1) capable and competent staff, (2) a clearly defined organization aligned with functional responsibilities, (3) clearly defined lines of authority and (4) adequate support. Figures 2 and 3 are suggested organizations that best satisfy these requirements for effective operations.

All state agencies in accordance with the responsibilities outlined in the Clean Air Act, as amended in 1970, have comprehensive responsibilities for the prevention and control of air pollutant emissions. The organization and functional responsibilities of local agencies will vary depending on their role in the state's total control plan. In the larger urban areas, the local control agency will generally assume comprehensive responsibility similar to the state agency. At the other end of the scale, minimal agencies will assume responsibility for specified field surveillance, inspection and enforcement activities. The organization should reflect the functional responsibility. In all instances the state agency must fill all program voids in addition to prescribing guidance, leadership and coordination to the local agencies.

Figure 1 DEPARTMENT OF ENVIRONMENTAL QUALITY
STATE OF OREGON (JANUARY 1971)

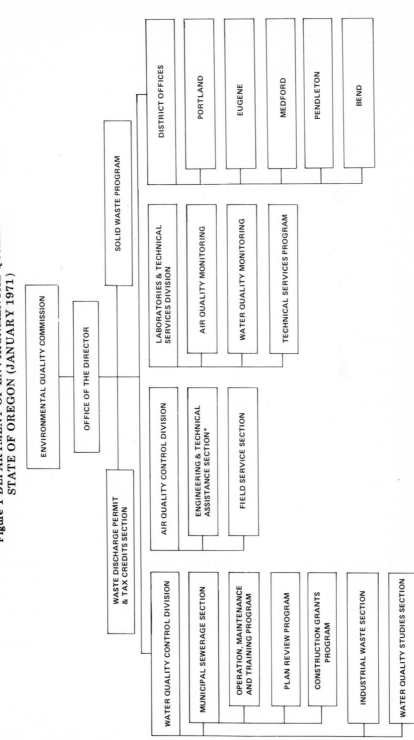

* Includes Enforcement Activities

Figure 2 SUGGESTED ORGANIZATIONAL STRUCTURE OF AN AIR POLLUTION CONTROL AGENCY

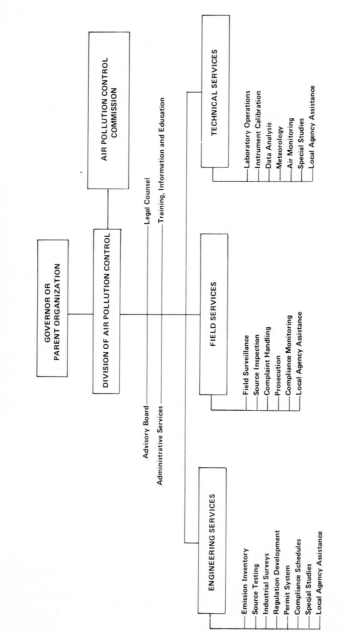

Note: Local Agency Assistance and coordination may be elevated to a fourth program unit if warranted.

Figure 3 TYPICAL ORGANIZATION CHART, FOR A LOCAL GOVERNMENTAL AIR POLLUTION CONTROL AGENCY

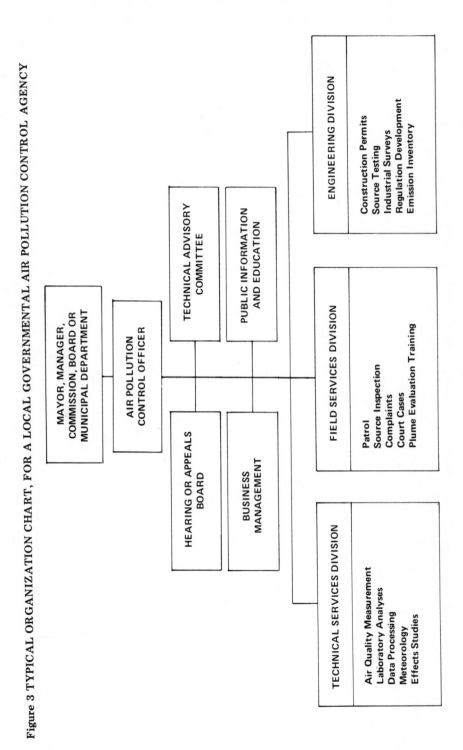

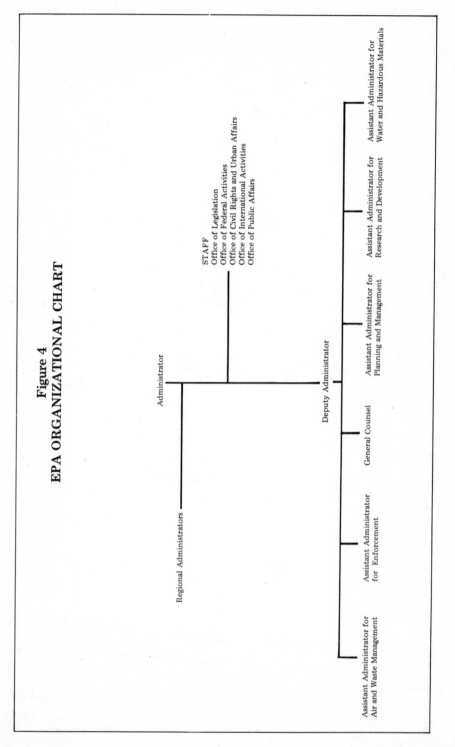

Figure 4
EPA ORGANIZATIONAL CHART

Administrator

Regional Administrators

STAFF
Office of Legislation
Office of Federal Activities
Office of Civil Rights and Urban Affairs
Office of International Activities
Office of Public Affairs

Deputy Administrator

Assistant Administrator for Air and Waste Management

Assistant Administrator for Enforcement

General Counsel

Assistant Administrator for Planning and Management

Assistant Administrator for Research and Development

Assistant Administrator for Water and Hazardous Materials

Figure 4
EPA ORGANIZATIONAL CHART
continued

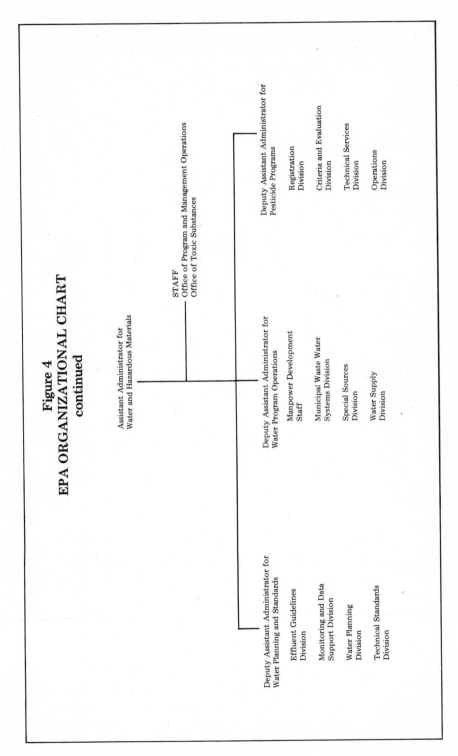

Assistant Administrator for
Water and Hazardous Materials

STAFF
Office of Program and Management Operations
Office of Toxic Substances

Deputy Assistant Administrator for
Water Planning and Standards

Effluent Guidelines
Division

Monitoring and Data
Support Division

Water Planning
Division

Technical Standards
Division

Deputy Assistant Administrator for
Water Program Operations

Manpower Development
Staff

Municipal Waste Water
Systems Division

Special Sources
Division

Water Supply
Division

Deputy Assistant Administrator for
Pesticide Programs

Registration
Division

Criteria and Evaluation
Division

Technical Services
Division

Operations
Division

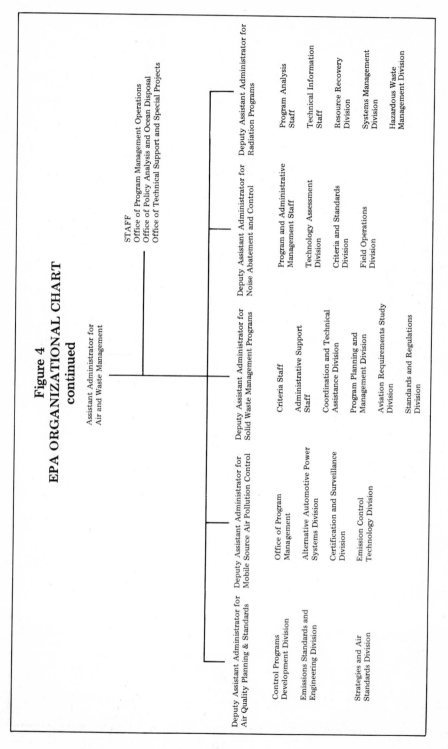

Figure 4
EPA ORGANIZATIONAL CHART
continued

Assistant Administrator for
Air and Waste Management

STAFF
Office of Program Management Operations
Office of Policy Analysis and Ocean Disposal
Office of Technical Support and Special Projects

Deputy Assistant Administrator for
Air Quality Planning & Standards

Control Programs
Development Division

Emissions Standards and
Engineering Division

Strategies and Air
Standards Division

Deputy Assistant Administrator for
Mobile Source Air Pollution Control

Office of Program
Management

Alternative Automotive Power
Systems Division

Certification and Surveillance
Division

Emission Control
Technology Division

Deputy Assistant Administrator for
Solid Waste Management Programs

Criteria Staff

Administrative Support
Staff

Coordination and Technical
Assistance Division

Program Planning and
Management Division

Aviation Requirements Study
Division

Standards and Regulations
Division

Deputy Assistant Administrator for
Noise Abatement and Control

Program and Administrative
Management Staff

Technology Assessment
Division

Criteria and Standards
Division

Field Operations
Division

Deputy Assistant Administrator for
Radiation Programs

Program Analysis
Staff

Technical Information
Staff

Resource Recovery
Division

Systems Management
Division

Hazardous Waste
Management Division

Figure 4
EPA ORGANIZATIONAL CHART
continued

General Counsel

Deputy General Counsel

Water Quality Division

Pesticides, Toxic Substances
and Solid Waste Management
Division

Air Quality, Noise, and
Radiation Division

Grants, Contracts, and General
Administration Division

Figure 4
EPA ORGANIZATIONAL CHART
continued

Assistant Administrator for
Enforcement

STAFF
Office of Program and Management Operations
Office of Technical Analysis

Deputy Assistant Administrator for
Water Enforcement

Permit Programs Division

Review and Coordination
Division

Enforcement Proceedings
Division

Deputy Assistant Administrator for
General Enforcement

Mobile Source Enforcement
Division

Stationary Source
Enforcement Division

Pesticides Enforcement
Division

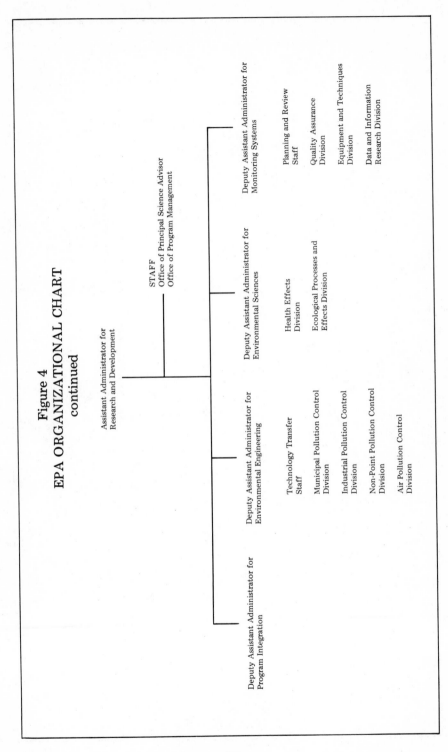

Figure 4
EPA ORGANIZATIONAL CHART
continued

Assistant Administrator for
Research and Development

STAFF
Office of Principal Science Advisor
Office of Program Management

Deputy Assistant Administrator for
Program Integration

Deputy Assistant Administrator for
Environmental Engineering

Technology Transfer
Staff

Municipal Pollution Control
Division

Industrial Pollution Control
Division

Non-Point Pollution Control
Division

Air Pollution Control
Division

Deputy Assistant Administrator for
Environmental Sciences

Health Effects
Division

Ecological Processes and
Effects Division

Deputy Assistant Administrator for
Monitoring Systems

Planning and Review
Staff

Quality Assurance
Division

Equipment and Techniques
Division

Data and Information
Research Division

75

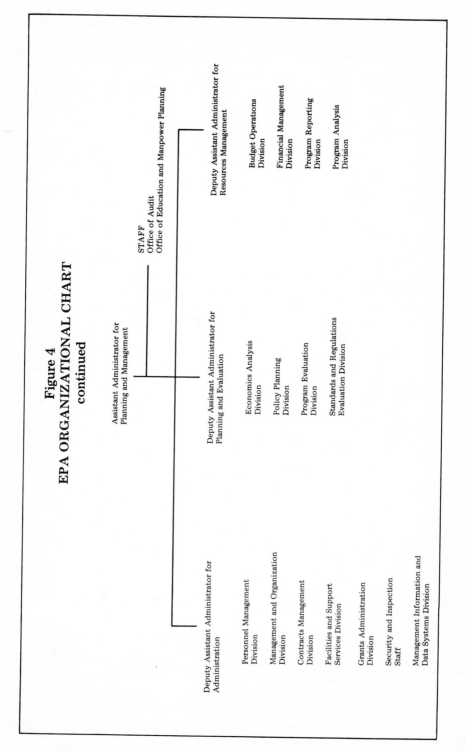

Figure 4
EPA ORGANIZATIONAL CHART
continued

Assistant Administrator for
Planning and Management

STAFF
Office of Audit
Office of Education and Manpower Planning

Deputy Assistant Administrator for
Administration

Personnel Management
Division

Management and Organization
Division

Contracts Management
Division

Facilities and Support
Services Division

Grants Administration
Division

Security and Inspection
Staff

Management Information and
Data Systems Division

Deputy Assistant Administrator for
Planning and Evaluation

Economics Analysis
Division

Policy Planning
Division

Program Evaluation
Division

Standards and Regulations
Evaluation Division

Deputy Assistant Administrator for
Resources Management

Budget Operations
Division

Financial Management
Division

Program Reporting
Division

Program Analysis
Division

76

Chapter Eight
Industry— Control
Agency Relationships

VIII. INDUSTRY-CONTROL AGENCY RELATIONSHIPS

The primary responsibility for regulating the emission of air pollutants at the source rests with State and local air pollution control agencies. Therefore, the relationship between industry and these agencies is of great importance.

The responsibility for reducing or curtailing air pollution falls on the enforcement branch of the air pollution control agency. This mission can only be accomplished by means of direct and frequent contact with the owners and operators of the sources of air pollution in order to ensure the widespread use of the best of the available control technology. Enforcement of the rules and regulations is the primary mechanism for achieving this goal. Both the standards contained in the rules and regulations and the procedures used in their enforcement, therefore, should be clear and certain from the standpoint of both voluntary and compulsory compliance.

Many administrative, legal and technical factors must be considered in attempting to achieve mass compliance on a large scale at the earliest possible time.

Field operations initiate the enforcement process by establishing whether or not individual emission sources comply with the rules and regulations. To meet this objective, enforcement personnel perform the following functions:

- *Notification.* Apprise all affected owners and operators of compliance requirements.
- *Surveillance.* Detect, observe and identify all emission sources.
- *Inspection.* Enter facilities and inspect all emission sources to determine compliance and gather information pertinent to factors causing emissions, conduct necessary emission and other tests, collect evidence, issue violation notices or citations and promote voluntary compliance.

The term "compliance" means that a source does not violate any rules and regulations. At least 3 statutes of compliance should be distinguished:

- *Continuing Compliance*—the realization of a source emission reduction plan or emission limit requirements on a continuing, long-term basis. Continuing compliance implies confidence that the facility is operating with little or no risk of violation and requires minimal surveillance.

- *Functional Compliance*—the status of a facility only at the time it is observed or inspected by a field enforcement officer. A facility is in technical compliance whenever insufficient information or evidence is available to justify serving a violation notice or citation even though non-compliance may be suspected. This includes situations where source testing or special investigations may be required to make a definitive compliance determination.
- *Non-Compliance*—any violation of a rule or regulation supported by valid information and evidence and justifying the issuance of a violation notice or citation.

Thus, any individual observation or inspection of an emission source results in 1 of 2 determinations: (1) compliance, (2) non-compliance (violation). These necessitate two distinct processing procedures. Reports of compliance (both continuing and functional) are reviewed, processed and rescheduled for inspection. Functional compliance cases, particularly those where violations are suspected, are assigned higher surveillance and inspection frequencies, or require special follow-up action, such as source testing. Where non-compliance is established, violation notices are issued, reviewed and processed towards legal action until continuing compliance is achieved.

The handling of functional compliance cases is the greatest problem facing enforcement personnel. While violations of visible emission standards and permit infractions are relatively easy to demonstrate, violations due to grain loading, process weight, fuel composition or standards regulating gaseous pollutants are more difficult and require special handling. Compliance determinations in these cases are made after sufficient information is gathered by the field enforcement officer on the design, operation and maintenance of the equipment. This is accomplished by gathering information on the *inspection points* appropriate to each class of source. The information collected may establish the requirement for fuel and material sampling, review of facility plans and operational data, and the performance of special emission source tests or ambient air monitoring. The enforcement officer should recommend appropriate sampling methods in order to obtain data that show whether or not the emission source is in continuing compliance through all ranges of its operation.

Enforcement action is indicated whenever a notice of violation or citation has been issued or whenever a report has been written that establishes all of the facts and evidence necessary to prove the occurrence of a violation of the rules and regulations. The objective of enforcement is to bring all sources which are in violation into a continuing compliance status as soon as possible.

There are variations in the processing of violation notices and reports among a number of air pollution control agencies. Even within one agency, alternative paths to compliance short of, and/or including, legal action may be provided for. These will depend on the history of the agency, the powers delegated to it, the stage of its development and its administrative skills.

Alternative 1. Administrative Conferences and Hearings.

The owner or operator of a facility in violation is requested to attend an administrative conference or hearing, usually at control agency headquarters. *Informal* or preliminary hearings are presided over by enforcement agency staff members. *Formal* hearings may be presided over by the air pollution control officer, a hearing master or hearing board. The owner may cooperate by agreeing to correct the problem or to prepare a compliance plan or schedule. The facility is periodically inspected by field enforcement officers to establish if the problem has been corrected according to schedule. If repeated violations occur, the case may be prosecuted in the courts. Administrative conferences may also be conducted at the facility.

Alternative 2. Notice-to-Courts Route

In this procedure, the preparation of a written notice automatically leads to the preparation of a misdemeanor complaint and prosecution in the courts. Investigation is generally conducted to confirm field evidence and source ownership and responsibility.

Alternative 3. Variance.

This alternative is a procedure which is initiated by a facility which has knowledge of compliance requirements and wishes to obtain a variance from the affected rules and regulations in order to correct an air pollution problem. The owner petitions a hearing board for a variance from an affected rule or regulation to correct its emission problem. The hearing board may either grant or deny the variance. The granting of the variance usually will depend on the problem, the equities involved and the preparation of a compliance plan. Compliance with the terms of the variance is checked by the field enforcement officer.

Alternative 4. Permit Systems.

This alternative is employed by enforcement agencies that operate permit systems. Where a permit or certificate to operate equipment is granted, but the equipment is found later to repeatedly violate the rules and regulations, the air pollution control agency may petition the hearing board to revoke the permit. Similarly, the owner of the equipment may petition a hearing board, with cause, if an agency denies a permit application.

The compliance path that should be used depends on the nature of the violation. Some violations may be due to negligence and are easily corrected through improved equipment operation or maintenance. Others may be due to difficult engineering problems which may be costly and difficult to correct. In the latter case, some form of negotiated compliance plan should be prepared by the owner of the equipment and evaluated by the control agency.

The compliance plan thus may be the result of an administrative conference, a hearing board action or a court action. The procedure selected should be one which provides for decisiveness and speed in reaching the desired compliance. Care must be taken, however, in adopting enforcement procedures which, because of appeals and court reversals, ultimately diminish the legal authority of the agency. The legal history and precedents established by an air pollution control agency are as much an integral part of the legal authority as the written law which it enforces.

Enforcement

Most enforcement of standards or regulations under the Clean Air Act is not done in court. Although a few court cases have received the lion's share of publicity, the bulk of the work remains administrative. The Department of Justice represents EPA in legal actions. The Administrator may notify a polluter that he is in violation of the law, issue an order to stop the pollution, and then seek an abatement action in court. If a violation occurs due to State inaction, EPA may notify the State and enforce abatement itself. It may also enforce State implementation plans. EPA may delegate any other enforcement responsibility to any State that has adequate enforcement procedures of its own. Any polluter who knowingly violates a regulation or order issued by EPA or a State implementation plan may be subject to fines or imprisonment on the Federal level.

In order to develop and enforce standards, the Administrator may require persons or firms which cause pollution to keep records, make reports, and test emissions. He may also enter and inspect the premises of the emission source if necessary. Consistent with the general agency policy, information obtained by EPA is available to the public for inspection, with the single exception of trade secrets.

Chapter Nine
Economics of Control

IX. ECONOMICS OF CONTROL

Various predictions have been made as to the cost of pollution control over future years. Although they differ, they have in common the fact they are expressed in terms of hundreds of billions of dollars.

Unfortunately, no precise system of making evaluations of cost-benefit relationships in the air pollution control field has yet been devised. In a field susceptible to emotionalism, it is easy to generate pressures for expenditures beyond those needed to achieve reasonable goals. Since this type of expenditure is generally non-productive, yields no revenues let alone profits, and reduces productivity in terms of invested capital, it must result in an upward push on the prices which consumers must pay for products. However, because of the complexity of the price decision-making process within each company, it is impossible to measure the exact amount of this push. Some have sought to minimize the impact of pollution control expenditures by saying they are but a fraction of one percent of the Gross National Product. However, this is a completely fallacious approach since only about one-eighth of the GNP reflects value added by manufacturing.

McGraw-Hill Company reports that American industry spent over $5 billion for new air and water pollution control facilities in 1973, and over $6 billion in 1974. This does not include the hundreds of millions of dollars spent each year on operation and maintenance of billions of dollars of pollution control facilities already in place.

As for future projections, the Council on Environmental Quality states that there are many types of costs associated with a degraded environment and with programs undertaken to improve it. The cost of a degraded environment is measured in damages to health, vegetation, materials, and other values or in the costs that we incur to avoid these damages. Remedial action also has costs — costs of abatement and transaction costs for monitoring and for enforcement.

The magnitude of these costs, their impact, and their distribution are critical to evaluating environmental policy alternatives and to developing strategies for their timely implementation.

It is clear that our national commitment to a cleaner environment will be very costly — about $275 billion during the next decade. It will total about 2.5 percent of our gross national product during this period. However, stating the economic burden in such "macro-economic" terms tends to belittle and obscure the very real economic impacts which pollution control laws and regulations have on small business enterprises.

On November 5, 1974, Raymond E. Walk, Business Manager and Marketing Director of Modern Casting, a publication of the American Foundrymen's Society, wrote to Frank T. Schultz, Purchasing Agent, City of Green Bay, Wisconsin, in part as follows:

"Adding to these higher costs foundries must pass along, are the extraordinary high costs incurred by the local and federal Environmental Protection Agencies. The state of Wisconsin is a good example of their impact. During the past five years, Wisconsin has lost 10% of its foundries and I don't pretend that my records are complete, but these closings are verified. A list is enclosed. Also enclosed is correspondence showing two more Wisconsin foundries being forced out of business. This pattern is consistent throughout the United States. Newer foundries opening in less stringent states neither increase total national capacity for casting production nor replace the serious loss of expertise."

The list referred to by Mr. Walk contains some 375 foundries which have been closed over the past five years. The Wisconsin foundries referred to by Mr. Walk as having closed are 20 in number as follows:

Closed Foundries	Location	Date
South Water Foundry	Milwaukee, WI	Dec., 1968
SPO/C-E Cast	Milwaukee, WI	1969
Zenith Foundry Co.	Milwaukee, WI	Oct., 1969
Allis-Chalmers Mfg. Co.	Appleton, WI	Sept., 1970
Chicago Hardware Foundry	Racine, WI	1970
Falls Non-Ferrous Foundry	Sheboygan Falls, WI	Nov., 1970
Rohde Manufacturing Co.	Milwaukee, WI	1970-1971
Standard Brass Works	Milwaukee, WI	1970
Standard Ductile & Gray Iron Fdy.	Racine, WI	June, 1970
Giddings & Lewis-Kaukauna Fdy.	Kaukauna, WI	Dec., 1971
Highway Trailer Industries, Inc.	Edgerton, WI	July, 1971
Iroquois Foundry Co.	Racine, WI	1970-1971
Sivyer Steel Casting Co./Mitchell	Milwaukee, WI	March, 1971
United Foundry Co.	Grafton, WI	1970-1971
Acme Foundry Co.	Superior, WI	Dec., 1972
American Skein & Foundry Co.	Racine, WI	1972
International Harvester Co.	Milwaukee, WI	Sept. 1972
Kenosha Brass & Aluminum Fdy.	Kenosha, WI	Sept., 1973
Lakeside Malleable & Gray Iron	Racine, WI	Jan., 1973
Westphal Co.	Hayward, WI	March, 1974

"An Open Letter From Wisconsin Foundrymen," to Senator Muskie from G. P. Antonic, President, United Foundrymen of Wisconsin, printed in the Gray and Ductile Iron News, October, 1974, reads as follows:

Dear Senator Muskie:

Now that Congress has started to reevaluate the restrictive provisions of the Clean Air Act, I thought you should know why the foundry industry has suffered under its severe impact.

Prior to the time that any clean air legislation existed, it was publicly acknowledged that our industry produced less than 1% of total particulate emissions in the United States. In highly concentrated industrial areas the foundry contribution of particulates rose to 1½% of the total.

In 1966 federally sponsored interstate studies recommended a national clean air goal of 75 micrograms of particulate matter per cubic meter of air. According to the studies industry was to reduce its emissions by an average of 71.3%. Our Wisconsin state law, at .45 pounds per 1000 pounds of gas, is far stricter than this suggested goal and demands an actual reduction of 82%. What does this mean? The normal processing of one ton of iron within a cupola with no pollution controls produces an average of 18-20 pounds of particulate. The recommended 71.3% reduction would have removed 8.56 pounds of this particulate leaving 3.44 pounds to be emitted. Legislation, as passed, required an 82% reduction removing 9.84 pounds as opposed to 8.56 pounds; a difference of 1.28 pounds, but, at what cost?

Comparing the costs to remove this extra 1¼ pounds of particulate, we find the required investment for the equipment for a 71.3% reduction would have been approximately $50,000 for a ten ton per hour cupola as opposed to a $300,000 installation for 82% abatement. This is a lot of money for a small foundry, and one should know that the majority of foundries employ less than 100 people and are privately owned.

It would require fifty horsepower to run the 71.3% efficiency operation as opposed to 300 horsepower for the 82% operation. The annual electric bill to operate the 82% unit on a single shift operation is in excess of $10,000. An electric utility, in order to supply power to run this added 250 horsepower, must burn an additional 750,000 pounds of coal per year. And in so doing emits as much pollution to the atmosphere as was reduced by going from 71.3% to 82%, giving us a net gain of zero. Can we honestly say to ourselves that this additional amount of captured dust is worth the price?

Natural gas is also used to fuel afterburners in many foundry pollution control systems. This raises several questions:

1. Will enough energy become available to permit year around operation of the high energy system in the future?

2. If the answer to this question is no, then would it not be sensible to think in terms of low energy, low cost pollution control equipment producing a year round average of 3.4 pounds per ton?

The answers to these questions should come into sharp focus when one looks at the example provided by the recently forced shutdown of the pollution control system of one Wisconsin foundry due to a shortage of natural gas. The fuel saved was sufficient to supply 200 homes with heat for an entire year, and the power saved is enough to supply 24 homes with enough electricity for an entire year. This illustration is for just one of the 200 foundries in Wisconsin.

During 1974 and the years that follow, the foundry industry will continue to face up to the reality of the need for a clean environment to preserve and improve our quality of life. All we ask is that as you deliberate on such matters as the environmental impact of our industry that you also give equal weight to the economic considerations and the real net gain. Only in this way will we achieve a sound social and economic balance in developing environmental legislation. This can only be done if you will call on qualified people for assistance. We have these qualified people in our industry, and we want to give you that assistance. Between us we can develop means to keep air contamination within realistic limits, so we can end the massive waste of resources demanded by present standards.

Very truly yours,

UNITED FOUNDRYMEN OF WISCONSIN
G. P. Antonic, President

Following are excerpts from a statement filed by the American Foundrymen's Society and the Cast Metals Federation with the Permanent Subcommittee on Investigations of the Senate Committee on Government Operations:

Castings represent the very beginning of all manufacturing processes. The sudden loss of a relatively small number of foundries producing strategic castings could result in the total shutdown of the U.S. manufacturing complex, driving unemployment to unbelievable proportions. This could happen while government statistics show the industry shipping record tonnages. Eighty percent of all casting production finds direct use in manufacturing, one hundred percent some indirect use. Solutions to many of the current national problems are directly related to the health and stability of the foundry industry. . . .

The chief alloy imports into the U.S. have been chrome based, ferrosilicon, ferromanganese and silicon manganese products. Imports were sold in the U.S. market at such a reduced, non-competitive price that domestic producers could not afford capital investment for increased production. Two successive dollar devaluations, price controls and general increase in world production have reduced these imports to serious levels. These two factors have resulted in very low production capacity on the domestic scene. In addition, each domestic producer is forced to make changes to comply with EPA and OSHA standards. As furnaces are equipped to meet codes, effective capacity is curtailed by approximately 15%. As new installations are constructed, many modified existing units will be closed, leaving us with basically the same capacity. Ferrosilicon is particularly in short supply. . . .

Refractories are another area being affected by OSHA. There is a world-wide shortage of raw magnesite used in refractories in steel foundries and arc furnaces. In the U.S. this material is produced synthetically. Delivery is running approximately two years, energy availability being given as chief cause of the shortage. Other refractory products, such as fire clay and silica brick, are running into problems of lengthening lead time despite availability of raw materials. . . .

Prime metallurgical coal, a third raw material, used in the coking process has been committed to export. Since 1965 over 500 coking ovens have been closed and dismantled, representing a loss in capacity of 5,150 tons per day in production. A continuing battle with environmental agencies has further restricted production. Current expansion plans see no possible relief for five years. . . .

Electric melting was initially presented as a major solution to environmental problems in foundries. Current shortfalls of electric power prohibit foundries in many cases from operating at capacity levels let along increasing their capacity potential or productivity. . . .

The foundry industry does not challenge the concepts of legislative acts such as EPA and OSHA, but only the manner in which these new laws are being implemented. It has accelerated the loss of what is erroneously termed "marginal shops" but in reality is the cause that has effected this serious loss of expertise. Such foundries have been pushed to expend capital to meet conflicting and, in many cases immeasurable, standards with unproven control equipment, resulting in their management being involved in continuous litigation. The net results are: A major reduction in working capital, vast increases in non-productive operating costs, prohibitive escalation of energy consumption . . . all resulting in a severe restriction of their ability to add productive capacity. . . .

Economic impact studies conducted by the Environmental Protection Agency grossly underestimate the full cost of compliance to the industry. They rarely, if ever, include the high operating costs and the many exceptional variables which are encountered in installation, engineering, and sometimes relocation.

Heavy public relations activities by EPA have generated a multiplicity of citizen groups whose emotions have been allowed to adulterate the facts and further harass foundries. The sum spent on this activity exceeds the total the foundry industry musters annually for research and development.

The secondary effect of EPA regulations is often as great as the effect of the initial regulations. For example, prior to the promulgation of the Air Pollution Control regulations the foundry industry as a whole had no waste water problems. The air cleaning systems brought about voluminous water usage which in turn required installation of water treatment systems of a cost equal to the original air cleaning system.

The Occupational Safety and Health Act is enforced in an equally unrealistic manner. Foundries are literally forced to spend millions of dollars in areas of relatively minor hazards, leaving areas of major injuries unattended or given minor attention.

The concept of accounting in the U.S. is predicated on an accounting convention that assumes a stable monetary unit. This concept works against foundries who, particularly since the Second World War, have been shifting from a labor intensive industry to that of capital intensiveness. Inability to accumulate surplus profits to compensate for depreciation loss, obsolescent technology and modernization forced an increasing reliance on borrowed capital and leasing which escalated liabilities foundries had to carry.

The short run jobbing foundries whose technology generally lags behind the volume producers are most prone to the impact of recessions. It is in this area that the greatest loss in foundries has occurred. It is also this foundry that is considered a "marginal producer" but is important to small and specialty manufacturers for his wide variety of expertise in the manufacture of short run specialty castings. The declining trend was already apparent during the early 1960s, but its full impact was not felt until the implementation of EPA and OSHA.

It is apparent that some immediate action is required to alleviate the destructive trends cutting away at an important segment of the foundry industry . . . the independent jobbing foundries. We must, as an industry, maintain and enhance this expertise and critical capacity. The following remedies are suggested:

1. A five-year moratorium, with qualification, on EPA, OSHA and similar legislation affecting foundries. This valuable time is needed to:

   a. Establish realistic standards;

   b. Establish whether other more serious problems are created by compliance with these standards;

   c. Develop standards with reproducible results;

   d. Permit capital to be invested in hardware and processes needed to gain the necessary productivity.

2. Conduct economic impact studies for the foundry industry by an agency other than those who set standards.

3. Conduct realistic economic studies as to what level of efficiency is most practical to achieve.

4. Quick write-off or other subsidy for the extraordinary high costs of environmental control.

5. Investment allowance and accelerated write-off for capacity expansion.

Chapter Ten
References

X. REFERENCES

I. Variations in Air Quality

Much of this material was excerpted from "Field Operations and Enforcement Manual for Air Pollution Control, Volume I: Organization and Basic Procedures" APTD-1100, U.S. Environmental Protection Agency, August, 1972.

II. Pollutants

Most of this material was excerpted from "Field Operations and Enforcement Manual for Air Pollution Control, Volume I: Organization and Basic Procedures," APTD-1100, U.S. Environmental Protection Agency, August, 1972.

III. Control Equipment

Much of this material was excerpted from "Field Operations and Enforcement Manual for Air Pollution Control, Volume II: Control Technology and General Source Inspection," APTD-1100, U.S. Environmental Protection Agency, August, 1972.

IV. Measurement of Pollutants

Much of this material was excerpted from material published by the Research Appliance Company, Route 8, Allison Park, Pa. (Pittsburgh District).

V. Federal Legislation

This discussion is based on the Clean Air Amendments of 1970, Clean Air Act, 42 U.S.C. 1857 et seq; Public Law 91-604, 84 Stat. 1676, December 31, 1970.

VI. Federal Regulations

"National Primary and Secondary Air Quality Standards," 40 CFR 50, 36 F.R. 22384, Nov. 25, 1971.

"Requirements for Preparation, Adoption, and Submittal of Implementation Plans," 40 CFR 51, 36 F.R. 22398, Nov. 25, 1971.

"Standards of Performance For New Stationary Sources," 40 CFR PART 60, 36 F.R. 24877, December 23, 1971, as amended: 38 F.R. 13562, May 23, 1973; and 39 F.R. 9308, March 8, 1974.

"National Emission Standards For Hazardous Air Pollutants," 40 CFR PART 61, 38 F.R. 8826, April 6, 1973.

Some of the other air regulations promulgated by EPA are as follows:

"Approval and Promulgation of Implementation Plans," 40 CFR PART 52, 37 F.R. 10846, May 31, 1972. This section is amended frequently. The latest revision was 39 F.R. 42510, December 5, 1974.

"Air Quality Control Regions, Criteria, and Control Techniques" 40 CFR 81, 36 F.R. 22421, Nov. 25, 1971.

"Prevention of Significant Air Quality Deterioration" 40 CFR 52, 39 F.R. 42517, Dec. 5, 1974.

VII. Federal and State Agency Organization

This information was excerpted from "Field Operations and Enforcement Manual for Air Pollution Control, Volume I: Organization and Basic Procedures," APTD-1100, U.S. Environmental Protection Agency, August, 1972, and from "Finding Your Way Through EPA," U.S. Environmental Protection Agency, October, 1973.

VIII. Industry-Control Agency Relationships

This material was excerpted from "Field Operations and Enforcement Manual for Air Pollution Control, Volume I: Organization and Basic Procedures," APTD-1100, U.S. Environmental Protection Agency, August, 1972, and from "The Challenge of the Environment: A Primer on EPA's Statutory Authority," U.S. Environmental Protection Agency, December, 1972.

IX. Economics of Control

Much of this material was excerpted from the Fourth Annual Report of the Council on Environmental Quality, September, 1973.

For further information please contact:

FORREST I. RETTGERS
Senior Vice President
Policy/Program Division
    (202) 331-3754

DR. RICHARD P. NALESNIK
Vice President & Manager
Resources & Technology
Department
    (202) 331-3783

DANIEL W. CANNON
Director
Environmental Affairs
    (202) 331-3787

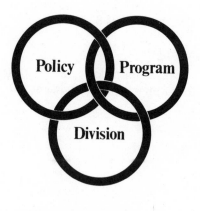